Fertility Awareness Mastery

CHARTING
WORKBOOK

LISA HENDRICKSON-JACK

Fertility Awareness Mastery

CHARTING WORKBOOK

FAHRENHEIT EDITION

A COMPANION TO

The Fifth Vital Sign

Publisher's note: This publication is designed to provide accurate and authoritative information in regard to the subject matter covered. The information herein is not intended to be a substitute for medical advice. It is sold with the understanding that neither the publisher nor the author is engaged in rendering medical, psychological, or other professional services. You are advised to seek the services of a competent health professional with regard to matters relating to your health.

The information in this book is not intended to treat, diagnose, cure, or prevent any disease. Neither the author, nor the publisher, accept liability of any kind for any damages caused, or alleged to be caused, directly or indirectly, from the use of the information in this book.

Although Lisa Hendrickson-Jack is a Justisse Method Holistic Reproductive Health Practitioner, this workbook does not provide instruction in any particular method of fertility awareness cycle tracking. It provides general information about fertility awareness-based methods. The charts included in the *Fertility Awareness Mastery Charting Workbook* can be used in conjunction with any fertility awareness-based charting modality. It is recommended that you seek support from a qualified fertility awareness instructor prior to applying the practices described in this book.

Published by Fertility Friday Publishing Inc.

For ordering information or special discounts for bulk purchases please contact: info@fertilityfriday.com.

Cover design: Simon Avery
Copy editing: Mary Ann Blair
Proofreading: Dana Nichols
Interior Design: Dino Marino

Spiral Bound ISBN: 978-1-9994280-5-1
Paperback ISBN: 978-1-9994280-3-7
Digital ISBN: 978-1-9994280-4-4

First edition, August 2019

Special Invitation

One thing that all women who chart our cycles have in common is that we all need the support of other women (who also chart their cycles!) to be successful. Over the years I've inspired thousands of women to dive headfirst into the exciting world of fertility awareness charting, and I'm thrilled that you've decided to join us.

As you embark on your charting journey, I'd like to personally invite you to join the Fertility Friday community for support and inspiration along the way at fertilityfriday.com/community.

You can also connect with me on Instagram @fertilityfriday, on Facebook at Facebook.com/fertilityfridays, and on Twitter @fertilefriday.

Contents

How to Use This Charting Workbook

So you're ready to start charting your cycles! Chances are you've read *The Fifth Vital Sign: Master Your Cycles and Optimize Your Fertility* and are now inspired to take the plunge. If you haven't yet read *The Fifth Vital Sign*, head over to thefifthvitalsignbook.com/amazon to grab your copy today. This workbook is not a "stand-alone" resource — you'll want to have both for best results.

I was inspired to create this workbook as a companion to *The Fifth Vital Sign* because I wanted to make it easy and practical for you to jump in and start charting your cycles right away! This book provides an alternative to the growing number of electronic charting apps on the market. Though most women prefer the convenience of entering their data right into their phones, I'm frequently reminded, when working with clients, that many women prefer paper charting. To my surprise, at least two or three out of every 10 women I work with opt to chart their cycles on paper! That is one of the main reasons I created this book. Some of us just love writing down our daily observations and keeping a physical record of our charts. If that's you, you'll love this book!

When I first started charting my cycles nearly 20 years ago, the smartphone technology we take for granted today (email, photos, videos, and apps) didn't even exist yet. That meant paper charting was the only option! So I created an Excel spreadsheet, printed it out, and off I went. Eventually I printed several years of charts and created a charting book for myself and my girlfriends. Those charts represented the very first iteration of the book you're now holding in your hands. Although technology has come a long way since then, and although styles of menstrual cycle charting have changed (and there are more apps and electronic devices than I can keep up with!), the fundamental information remains the same. Menstrual cycle tracking involves observing your three main fertile signs (cervical mucus, basal body temperature, and cervical position), identifying your fertile days by paying attention to your mucus patterns, and confirming ovulation by cross-checking to ensure the signs match up.

One of the biggest benefits of paper charting is learning how to interpret your observations without any distractions. Unlike when using an app, there are no algorithms filling in information for you, predicting when you'll ovulate, or telling you when your period will arrive. Instead, it's up to you to check your fertile signs each day, record what you see, and interpret your data objectively to figure out what it all means. By doing this, you'll naturally rely less on predictions and calculations and focus your attention on your daily observations (which is where it should be!).

Learning how to chart on paper will also help you resist falling into "rhythm method thinking." Instead of trying to predict ovulation based on your previous cycle patterns, you'll learn to observe your fertile signs each day and determine whether or not today is fertile based on what you actually see. As you make your way through the charting pages in this book, you'll see the patterns and fluctuations unfold as the weeks, months, and years go by. You'll see that ovulation doesn't always happen on the same day of your cycle. You'll see how diet, exercise, stress, and sleep (among other factors) affect your cycle. But most importantly, you'll see that it's possible to chart your cycles accurately (and effectively!) regardless of how "regular" or "normal" your cycles are.

As you continue to gain charting experience, you'll soon discover that your three main fertile signs (cervical mucus, basal body temperature, and cervical position) are only the beginning. You may wish to chart additional signs such as breast tenderness, mood changes, food cravings, exercise, sleep, and so much more. This book will allow you to choose what you want to pay attention to by customizing your charts with the details that are important to you.

A paper charting system gives you a physical reminder to record your fertile signs each day. Leave it on your night stand, your bathroom counter, or any other place that will help you remember to record your observations on a daily basis. Ideally, you'll want to write down your observations at the end of each day so they're fresh in your mind. Consider making charting your cycles a part of your bedtime routine so it becomes a habit — something you don't even need to think about anymore (like brushing your teeth).

The Fertility Awareness Mastery Charting Workbook provides you with your own personalized menstrual cycle charting system; using it will help you stay on track as you embark on your fertility awareness journey. This charting workbook will allow you to connect with this vital aspect of yourself and discover the connection between your *fifth vital sign* and your overall health.

Note that there are a number of fertility awareness-based methods including the method described in *Taking Charge of Your Fertility*, the Justisse Method, the Billings Ovulation Method®, the Marquette Model, the FEMM™ method, SymptoPro™, the Creighton Model FertilityCare System™, and many others. There are also a number of devices and apps on the market that use a variety of fertility awareness-based charting techniques. This book does not present any one specific method but instead presents a general overview of fertility awareness cycle tracking. It is recommended that you seek support from a qualified fertility awareness instructor when you're ready to embark on your own charting journey (see the resources section on page 112 for details).

What Is Fertility Awareness?

The Fifth Vital Sign explains that fertility awareness (FA) is central to the overall message that regular ovulation and menstruation are both crucial for optimal health regardless of whether or not you ever plan to have children. FA allows you to accurately identify and interpret your fertile signs. Many of us were taught that we could get pregnant on every single day of our cycles — that there are no "safe" days. However, you're only fertile on approximately six days of your cycle, and you can identify your fertile days by paying attention to the cyclical changes in your mucus, basal body temperature, and cervical position.[1]

When you understand how to identify your fertile window, you can avoid pregnancy naturally, optimize your chances of conception, and monitor your overall health and fertility — all while avoiding unnecessary exposure to the synthetic hormones found in most modern methods of birth control. When used correctly, the sympto-thermal method of FA (tracking cervical mucus, basal body temperature, and cervical position) is up to 99.4 percent effective in preventing pregnancy, putting it on par with hormonal contraceptives as far as effectiveness is concerned.[2]

Given that hormonal contraceptives are associated with a slew of harmful side effects including an increased risk of blood clots and stroke, anxiety, depression, low libido, clitoral and ovarian shrinkage, painful sex, nutrient deficiencies, and a delay in the return of your normal fertility, FA is a welcome alternative for many women.[3] FA awards you the same level of effectiveness and has no short- or long-term impact on your fertility. There's no transition period when you're ready to start a family; you simply start having unprotected sex on your fertile days. In that way, FA preserves your fertility.

There's something inherently powerful about not having to rely on doctors and drugs to manage your fertility. It may sound like it's too good to be true, but I assure you it's not. After using FA as my primary birth control method for nearly 20 years, and teaching hundreds of women to do the same, I can attest that any woman who desires to use this method (and is willing to take the necessary time to learn it) can use it successfully. Let's start by reviewing the three main fertile signs.

Cervical Mucus

Cervical mucus (CM) is a hydrogel produced by your cervix as you approach ovulation.[4] During your preovulatory phase, you're considered fertile on all of the days that you produce CM for two main reasons:

1. CM is the perfect pH for sperm.
2. CM keeps sperm alive for up to five days as you approach ovulation.[5]

You produce two main types of CM during your fertile window: clear and stretchy *peak mucus* and lotiony, white *non-peak mucus*.[6]

Peak mucus is described by a number of fertility awareness-based methods including the Justisse Method, the Billings Ovulation Method®, the FEMM™ method, and the Creighton Model FertilityCare System™. It refers to mucus that is clear, stretchy, and/or slippery/lubricative, has the quality of raw egg whites, and typically forms a thin thread when you stretch it between your fingers ("*spinnbarkeit*" is a German word that is used to describe this thread). When you have peak mucus, you'll notice that it feels lubricative when you wipe yourself before or after using the bathroom, and you may experience an obvious feeling of wetness throughout the day.

Non-peak mucus is cloudy or white in colour and doesn't stretch very much between your fingers. It's similar to the quality of creamy white hand lotion, and many FA resources will refer to non-peak mucus as having a creamy or sticky texture. Non-peak mucus doesn't have the spinnbarkeit thread-like quality of peak mucus and doesn't stretch very much between your fingers at all.

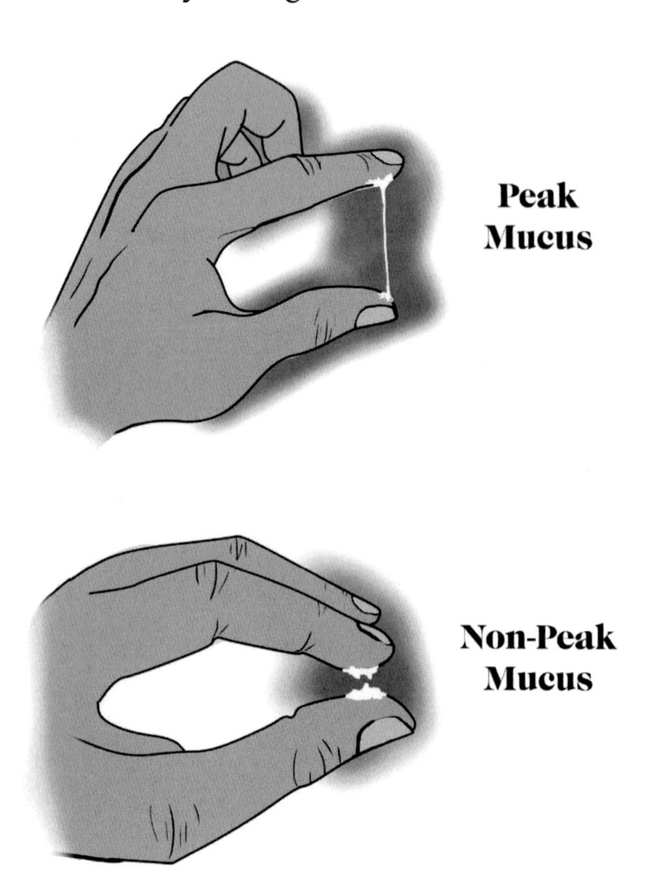

Basal Body Temperature

BBT is a measure of your resting (or baseline) metabolism. When you measure your basal body temperature (BBT) each morning and then plot it on a graph, you'll notice a clear difference between your preovulatory and postovulatory temperatures. Your progesterone levels rise after ovulation, and this causes your BBT to rise and remain high for the rest of your cycle. This is called a *sustained thermal shift*. Your temperatures will drop back down again 10 to 16 days after ovulation (unless you're pregnant), and you'll start a new cycle once your period arrives (refer to page 10).

Cervical Position

Your cervix is the lower part of your uterus. It fully dilates during labour to allow the baby to pass through the birth canal, and it dilates slightly at other times to allow menstrual blood, cervical mucus, and sperm to flow through. As you approach ovulation, estrogen causes your cervix to soften, open, and move to a higher position in your vagina, while progesterone causes your cervix to sit lower in your vagina and feel firm and closed. In fact, if you zoom the lens out, you'll find that your entire uterus is shifting position, causing your cervix to tilt backward or forward depending on where you are in your cycle (refer to pages 16 and 17 for more information on cervical position charting).

Charting Your Cervical Mucus

For most women, understanding their CM pattern is the most challenging part of learning FA. Most FA resources contain relatively vague instructions for both observing and recording CM. For instance, many of the available resources don't fully explain how to determine *sensation*. Although most talk about the significance of dry days, they don't typically describe how to tell the difference between dry, smooth, and lubricative sensations.[7]

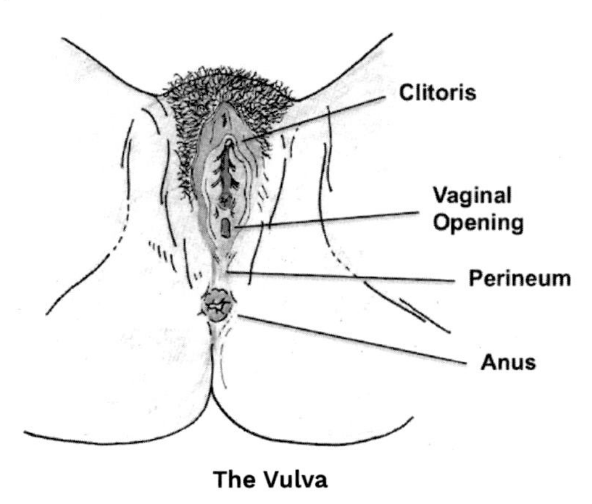

The Vulva

Sensation is one of the most misunderstood aspects of fertility awareness-based methods. Many women believe that sensation refers to an elusive "feeling" you get as you walk around throughout the day. However, the sensation I am referring to is much more literal. Sensation refers to the way it feels when you wipe your vulva with toilet paper. A number of fertility awareness-based methods describe a method of checking for CM with toilet paper including the Justisse Method, the FEMM method, and SymptoPro. The next time you go to the bathroom, take a piece of toilet paper, fold it flat, and wipe your vulva from front to back.

Pay close attention to how it feels as you wipe the toilet paper across your perineum (the smooth patch of skin between your vaginal opening and your anus, as shown in the image to the left). You'll notice a dry, smooth, or lubricative sensation. Understanding sensation makes it much easier to identify the difference between dry days and mucus days.

The key to understanding your mucus observations involves the following three steps:

1. Know the difference between a dry day and a mucus day,
2. Check for mucus regularly throughout the day, and
3. Record what you see.

Know the difference between a dry day and a mucus day

Since the "dry" in dry days refers to the sensation you feel when you wipe yourself, if you're not wiping yourself when you check for mucus, by definition, you will never feel a dry sensation (or have a dry day). Many women check for mucus by inserting their finger into their vagina to see if any mucus comes out on their finger. This is referred to as internal checking. The problem with this way of checking is that your vagina is *never* dry. Whenever you insert your finger into your vagina you'll *always* find moisture, leaving most women at a loss for what it really means to have a dry day. To set the record straight, a dry day is a day when you feel either a dry (or smooth) sensation when you wipe yourself and there's nothing on the toilet paper that you can stretch between your fingers. A mucus day, on the other hand, is a day when you can see mucus on your toilet paper and you can pick it up and stretch it between your fingers. You'll know it's a mucus day when you wipe yourself and feel a lubricative sensation. That sensation tells you that you're making peak mucus even if you're not able to pick it up off the toilet paper and stretch it between your fingers.

Check for mucus frequently throughout the day

When you establish the habit of checking for mucus frequently throughout the day, it quickly becomes second nature. One of the quickest ways to establish a new habit is to add it to an already established habit. With that in mind, I want you to start wiping yourself — on purpose — both before *and* after you go to the bathroom. You already wipe yourself when you go to the bathroom; you're simply adding the new habit of checking for mucus to what you already do.

Record what you see

FA only works when you make your daily observations — *and then record them.* Simply observing your mucus patterns won't help you! You need a system to record your data, which is what we're going for with this workbook!

Common Questions About Cervical Mucus Charting

What are the main types of cervical mucus? Which type is most "fertile"?

There are two main types of CM (as previously described on page 3): the peak type, which is clear, stretchy, and/or lubricative when you wipe yourself (similar to raw egg whites), and the non-peak type, which doesn't stretch very much between your fingers and has a consistency similar to creamy white hand lotion. Both types of CM are considered *equally* fertile during the preovulatory phase of your menstrual cycle (as you approach ovulation). I encourage you not to think of your CM as either more or less fertile. When you observe CM during your preovulatory phase you are *fertile.* After all, you can't be more or less pregnant!

How does cervical mucus make me "fertile"?

CM keeps sperm alive up to five days.[8] That means you could observe CM (either type!), have unprotected sex, and conceive up to five days later once you ovulate. Put another way, you could have sex on Monday (after observing peak or non-peak CM), ovulate on Friday, and conceive on Friday because the sperm may *still* be alive and waiting for ovulation.

Is "sticky" mucus fertile?

In a word, yes. When you start observing "sticky" (non-peak, lotiony, or pasty) CM in your preovulatory phase, pregnancy is possible for three important reasons:

- Sperm can survive for up to five days in your CM;[9]
- You're officially in your fertile window, your estrogen levels are rising, and you are approaching ovulation; and
- Your cervix is officially open for business, and pregnancy is possible.

For these reasons, all preovulatory mucus is considered fertile, as unprotected sex on days of "sticky" mucus can result in pregnancy.

How much cervical mucus should I see? What is "normal"?

In a normal cycle you will produce CM (either type) for 2 to 7 days, with at least 1 day of peak mucus leading up to ovulation.[10] Although you might expect to see large quantities of mucus every day, you'll produce about one-quarter to one-half of a teaspoon of CM on your fertile days.[11]

Am I fertile if I only see a small amount of cervical mucus once during the day?

Yes! You are considered fertile on any day you observe CM prior to ovulation regardless of how much you see. When you see mucus it means you are in your fertile window, your cervix is open, you are approaching ovulation, and pregnancy is possible (refer back to *Is "sticky" mucus fertile?* on page 6).

How do I tell the difference between cervical mucus, vaginal cell slough, arousal fluid, and semen?

CM differs from other types of vaginal discharge (and semen) in a number of ways. Once you start charting your cycles it's important to learn how to tell the difference. (See Chapter 3 of *The Fifth Vital Sign* for a full discussion of the different types of vaginal discharge you may observe during your cycle.) Here are some basic differences:

- You produce *CM* as you approach ovulation; it will either be creamy and white like hand lotion or clear and stretchy like raw egg whites.
- *Vaginal cell slough* refers to the normal shedding of your vaginal cells. When you have vaginal cell slough you'll typically notice a smooth sensation when you wipe yourself with toilet paper. You may notice a shiny film on the toilet paper, or you may notice a crumbly white or yellow discharge in your underwear.
- *Arousal fluid* is situational, and you'll observe it at any point in your cycle when you experience arousal. Arousal fluid is lighter, tends to evaporate more quickly, and can't be stretched multiple times between your fingers.
- *Semen* is more difficult to distinguish from CM as it is typically cloudy and somewhat stretchy. Semen tends to be a bit musty, and will only be present the day after unprotected sex (see Chapter 10 of *The Fifth Vital Sign* for additional details).

Is it normal for my mucus to be yellow or gummy?

Mucus that is yellow tinged, gummy (like the goo on the back of a new credit card), or gluey (like sticky white glue) may be a sign of cervical inflammation and/or an infection; it isn't normal, though it is fairly common. If you consistently observe these types of CM, consider booking an appointment with your doctor and requesting a screen for infections (bacterial vaginosis [BV], yeast, STIs, etc.). Refer to Chapter 11 of *The Fifth Vital Sign* for more information on supporting cervical health.

I barely see any CM. Why don't I have more?

Not all women observe significant quantities of CM during their fertile window. Your CM production falls within the normal range if you produce mucus for 2 to 7 days prior to ovulation with at least 1 day of peak mucus (refer back to *How much cervical mucus should I see?* on page 6). A number of factors interfere with normal CM production including long-term hormonal contraceptive (HC) use, HPV, cervical dysplasia, cervical surgeries/procedures to remove abnormal cells, use of certain medications (including antihistamines and certain fertility drugs), and the natural aging process. Refer to Chapters 3 and 11 of *The Fifth Vital Sign* for a full discussion of the factors that affect CM production and the actions you can take to improve it.

If I'm on the pill (or using a hormonal contraceptive method like the patch, ring, or IUD), will I still see mucus?

No. One of the ways HCs prevent pregnancy is by preventing your cervical crypts from producing fertile-quality CM. HCs stimulate your cervix to fill with a thick mucus plug, which causes you to have only dry days. This plug prevents sperm from penetrating your cervix, thus preventing pregnancy. You'll only reliably observe CM when you're using non-hormonal birth control methods and are otherwise cycling normally.

I have CM almost every single day. Is that normal?

Observing CM continuously throughout your cycle falls outside what's considered normal. If you regularly observe CM outside of the 2 to 7-day window prior to ovulation, you'll want to look into it further. First, ensure you're recording your CM accurately. Many women overread their mucus by checking internally. Given that your vagina is never dry, checking internally may cause you to think you have mucus every day (when you may actually be observing your vaginal cell slough). When you wipe externally you'll have a more accurate sense of your mucus days versus your dry days.

If you're checking accurately and are still seeing mucus every day, it could be a sign of an infection (yeast or BV), abnormal cervical cells (as cervical dysplasia causes a non-lubricative watery discharge throughout the cycle), or a hormonal imbalance. Refer to Chapters 3 and 11 of *The Fifth Vital Sign* for details.

I'm using fertility awareness for birth control. How do I know which days are fertile by charting my mucus?

You are fertile on each day you observe CM prior to ovulation, plus the three days following your peak day (the last day you observe CM that is clear, stretchy, and/or lubricative). Refer to Chapters 5 and 10 of *The Fifth Vital Sign* for details.

Is it better to chart my mucus or use an ovulation predictor kit (OPK) to identify ovulation?

OPKs test for the luteinizing hormone (LH) surge you produce approximately 24 to 36 hours prior to ovulation. As such, they do not confirm that ovulation has happened — they simply indicate that you will *likely* ovulate within the next 24 to 36 hours.[12] OPKs often show a positive reading several days *after* you've started to observe CM. Since sperm can survive in your CM for up to five days, and you produce CM as you approach ovulation, OPKs should *always* come second to your mucus observations.

I'm trying to conceive. How will I know when the best time for sex is by charting my mucus?

The best time to have sex when you're trying to conceive is on any day of CM prior to ovulation. Your days of peak CM are *optimal* for conception, so make a point of having sex on any day you observe clear or stretchy mucus and/or have a lubricative sensation when you wipe.

How much mucus do I need to produce in order to get pregnant?

Although CM is crucial for natural conception, *it's possible to conceive during any cycle when ovulation takes place* — regardless of how much CM you observe. In addition to CM, conception is dependent on the quality of your eggs, the quality of his sperm, and your overall health. If his sperm is of poor quality, for example, having large quantities of mucus may not help you to conceive naturally. With that in mind, consider yourself fertile on any day you observe CM prior to ovulation, regardless of how much you see. You can't be "more" or "less" fertile on any given day — you're either fertile or you're not. Remember that when you see mucus it means you're approaching ovulation, your cervix is open for business, and pregnancy is possible.

Can I see mucus and not ovulate?

Yes, you can. You produce CM in response to rising estrogen levels as you approach ovulation. It's possible for your body to start gearing up for ovulation and then back down again. This phenomenon is called a double peak, and it occurs when you see several days of mucus followed by dry days (with no confirmed ovulation), and then at some point your mucus returns and you eventually ovulate later in your cycle. It's like your body was trying to ovulate but didn't quite get there. Since you can't predict ovulation ahead of time, you must consider all preovulatory days of CM fertile, even if they don't lead to ovulation. This can certainly cause frustration, especially if it's a pattern you frequently observe.

Can I have mucus during my period? Does that mean my period could be fertile?

Yes, it's possible to produce CM toward the end of your period, which means you should consider the light and very light days of your period *potentially* fertile.

Your hormone levels are too low to trigger CM production during the moderate and heavy days of your true menstrual period (when you have confirmed ovulation 12 to 14 days before), but it's possible for you to start producing CM as your period tapers off. This can happen in a short menstrual cycle (though you wouldn't know you're having a short cycle ahead of time).

In order to determine if the light and very light days of your period are fertile, simply check for CM to confirm if it's a mucus day or a dry day when you wipe.

Head over to thefifthvitalsignbook.com/bonuses to access a free training video I've put together that demonstrates how to check and chart your CM.

Charting Your BBT

The simplest way to measure your BBT is to take your temperature each morning before you get out of bed. Tracking CM and BBT together increases the effectiveness of FA because you can only confirm ovulation when these signs line up. Since your sustained thermal shift happens *after* ovulation, your BBT can only help you confirm ovulation, *not* predict it. Measuring your BBT also helps you predict when your period is coming because the number of days between ovulation and your period stays fairly constant.

You'll need a basal body thermometer that measures to two decimal places (e.g., 97.62°F). You can then round your temperature up or down accordingly (round up if 0.05 or higher, round down if 0.04 and lower). Take your temperature from one of three locations: orally, vaginally, or axillary (under your arm). Most women measure their temperature orally, so if you're unsure, start there, and follow these three steps to get an accurate reading:

1. **Take your temperature first thing each morning *before* you get out of bed after a minimum of five hours of consecutive sleep.**

For an accurate measure of your resting metabolism, you'll need to allow enough time for your body to "reset" itself. The best time to take your BBT is right after you wake up in the morning after you've slept for at least five consecutive hours.[13] If you jump out of bed and walk around before you take your temperature, you won't get an accurate reading. Try to leave your thermometer on your nightstand, or place it on top of your alarm clock (or phone!) as a reminder.

2. **Leave your thermometer in place for 10 minutes before pushing the button.**

Most of my clients want to skip this step when I first introduce it! Unfortunately, it makes a big difference. When you leave your thermometer in place for 10 minutes, you're allowing sufficient time for the thermometer to warm up in order for the temperature reading to stabilize. When you use a digital thermometer it typically beeps within 10 seconds. However, if you were to take your temperature three times in a row, you'd likely get three different readings. After a full cycle of taking their temperatures this way (commonly called temping), my clients consistently (albeit reluctantly) admit that their temperatures are more stable, with far fewer abnormal spikes and dips in their charts.

3. **Take your temperature around the same time each morning.**

Your BBT increases with every additional 30 minutes you sleep. If you wake up at 6 a.m. one morning and 10 a.m. the next, you'll notice a difference in your temperature. However, most people don't wake up at exactly the same time each day. From a practical standpoint, it's more important to get a good night's sleep than to wake up extra early just to take your temperature (see Chapter 13 of *The Fifth Vital Sign*). For that reason, my approach in this area is relaxed and realistic. Aim to take your temperature at about the same time each day. When you wake up earlier or later, or have a rough night's sleep, simply add a note to your chart with the time you woke up and a short explanation.

Many women have asked me if I think it's worth it for them to take their temperatures when they know it will be disrupted or questionable, and my answer is always *yes*. By taking and recording your temperature when it's not "perfect," you'll learn how your temperature is affected by life's disruptions. That's where the notes come in. By making accurate notes, you'll find it easier to interpret your temperatures when you review your chart, even when some of them are questionable. For the record, there's no such thing as a perfect chart. You'll *always* have one or more questionable temperature in every cycle. Your job is understanding how to work *with* the anomalies instead of pretending they're not there or trying to avoid having them in the first place.

Common Questions About BBT Charting

What factors affect my temperature readings?

Knowing which lifestyle factors can affect your temperature will make interpreting your charts much easier. The following is a list of the factors that may affect your BBT:

- Stress, illness, or fever
- Shift work, night wakings, or restless sleep
- Alcohol consumption the previous day
- Travel, flights, time zone changes, and daylight savings time changes
- Food allergies, seasonal allergies, and food sensitivities
- Taking your temperature after you've gotten out of bed
- Drinking water or tea in the morning before you take your temperature (orally)
- Switching how you take your temperature (i.e., from oral to underarm or vaginally)
- Switching thermometers mid-cycle

Some of these factors can dramatically affect one woman's BBT, whereas another woman won't notice much of a change. Your job is to figure out which factors affect *your* temperature (and make a note of it!) so you can accurately interpret your charts.

What kind of thermometer should I buy?

Look for a thermometer that measures to two decimal places (e.g., 97.24°F). You may find additional features such as a backlight, memory, the ability to shift between Celsius and Fahrenheit, and the ability to sync with your phone helpful, but they aren't necessary.

What is the difference between basal body temperature (BBT) and average sleep temperature?

Your average sleep temperature is calculated based on multiple readings of your body temperature as you sleep. A number of wearable devices are programed with algorithms that calculate your average sleep temperature, and they automatically adjust any abnormal temperature readings, thus giving the appearance of a "perfect" temperature chart every cycle.

This feature can be extremely helpful if you have a hard time remembering to take your temperature or if you consistently have disrupted sleep schedules (given that your *average sleep temperature* is equally helpful in confirming ovulation). However, if you were hoping to glean additional health information from these devices, you're out of luck.

Since your BBT is a measure of your baseline metabolism, it is receptive to a wide variety of changes including thyroid or other endocrine issues, stress, illness, allergies, food sensitivities, and more (as listed in the previous section). Many of the wearable devices will spit out a perfect-looking temperature chart regardless of any underlying health issues you may have (including thyroid disorders, endocrine or immune issues, and illness).

For that reason, you may wish to measure your BBT using an "old-fashioned" thermometer when you are seeking to glean additional health information from your charts.

What if I don't wake up at the same time every day?

As you jump into menstrual cycle charting, it's important to acknowledge that perfection is not the goal. Some days you'll wake up earlier or later, and some nights you won't sleep very well. Do your best to take your temperature within a two-hour window each day, but remember these two steps when you've woken up earlier or later than normal:

1. Hold your thermometer in place for a full 10 minutes prior to measuring your temperature, and
2. Note the time you woke up on your chart.

That's it! While some women find that their temperature significantly fluctuates when they get up earlier or later, others don't experience that. Taking your temperature correctly and noting your wake-up time on your chart are much more important than waking up at the exact same time each day. By doing so, you'll learn how to interpret your temperature more accurately, and you'll see firsthand how your temperature responds to the day-to-day realities of life.

Should I wake up early on the weekends so I can take my temperature at the same time as I usually do during the week?

Definitely not! The benefits of getting a full night's sleep outweigh the potential benefits of charting at the same time every day. I feel that charting should fit into your life — not the other way around! So instead of disrupting your sleep and forcing yourself to wake up at 5 a.m. on a Saturday to measure your temperature, just take your temperature when you wake up. If it happens to be an hour or two later, simply note your wake-up time on your chart (refer to the previous section for more information).

What if I work different shifts and sometimes sleep during the day?

To get an accurate temperature reading, you ideally need a minimum of five hours of consecutive sleep to allow your resting metabolism to "reset." When you work all night, you can still get an accurate measure of your resting metabolism provided you take your temperature after you've slept for at least five hours straight the following day. Note your wake-up time on your chart and how many hours you slept. As you record your temperatures you'll begin to see if (or how) shift work affects your cycles and how much your temperatures are affected by your varying wake-up times.

What if I get up to pee one or more times each night?

For some women, getting up to pee during the night will cause an obvious disruption in their temperature patterns. But since not going to the bathroom (when you need to) isn't an option, you'll need a strategy. Simply note sleep disruptions on your chart. Create a notation for yourself or use the comments section to mark when your sleep was disrupted and by how much. By noting your sleep disruptions, you'll have a better sense of how much they're affecting your temperatures.

What if I have young children who wake me up during the night and/or early in the morning?

When you have small children jumping into your bed throughout the night and/or first thing in the morning, it can be hard to remember to take your temperature — let alone get an accurate reading. Try leaving your thermometer in a place that's easy for you to access (and remember), such as your night stand, on top of your cell phone, on the headboard of your bed, or under your pillow. If your children disrupt your sleep, I would still encourage you to take your temperature in the morning when it's time to get out of bed. Note any sleep disturbances on your chart and you'll have a better idea of how your temperatures are affected. Many women in this situation find that wearable thermometers help them stay consistent with temperature taking, and having a device that measures average sleep temperature (and irons out the ups and downs) can make chart interpretation easier during this phase of life.

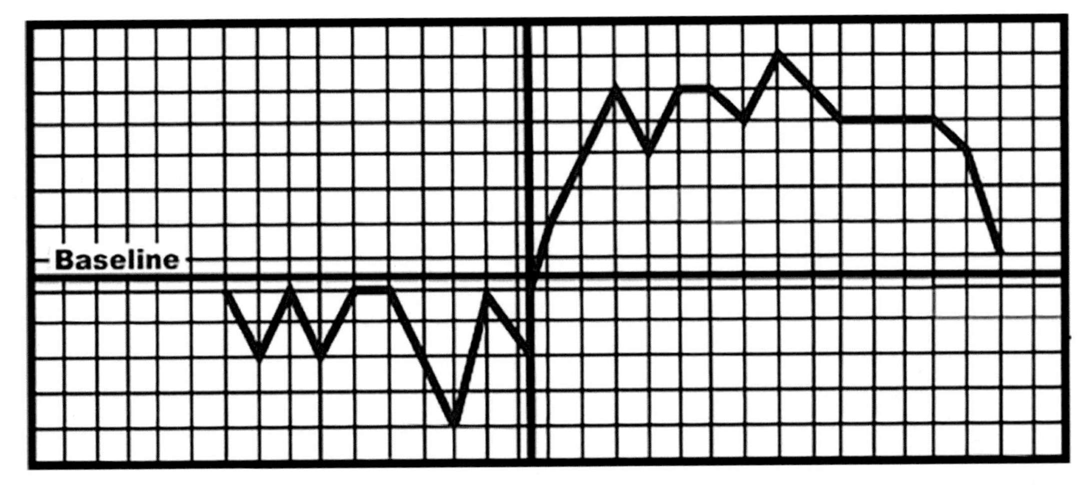

BBT Chart

What if I wake up an hour or two before my normal wake-up time? Should I take my temperature early or wait until I get up for the day?

If you wake up in the middle of the night, or you wake up earlier than your usual time (and you plan to go back to sleep), I recommend that you go back to sleep and wait until you're ready to get up for the day. Just note on your chart that you woke up in the middle of the night. Since getting enough good-quality sleep is more important than waking up early to take your temperature, it makes sense to prioritize sleep. And the last thing you want to do is wake yourself up more and possibly have difficulty getting back to sleep!

How do I know if my temperatures are normal?

Although your preovulatory BBTs will fluctuate, they should fall consistently around 97.5°F (36.4°C) or higher. Your postovulatory temperatures should fall consistently higher than your preovulatory temperatures, with at least one or more readings measuring higher than 98.0°F (37.0°C). If your preovulatory BBTs consistently measure below 97.5°F (36.4°C), you'll want to look into possible causes of low metabolism, including issues with the thyroid (refer to Chapter 16 of *The Fifth Vital Sign* for details).

How do I confirm ovulation with my BBT?

You're looking for a clear and obvious shift between your pre- and postovulatory temperatures. Anyone should be able to look at your chart and see the temperature shift. To confirm ovulation with your BBT you need three consecutive (normal) temperatures that are higher than the previous six (normal) preovulatory temperatures. *Normal* means temperatures that are not abnormally high due to illness, sleep disturbances, or any other factors. The baseline (also referred to as the coverline) refers to the line that divides the low and high temperatures. You draw the baseline *after* your temperature shift. As shown in the BBT chart above, the preovulatory temperatures are below the baseline, and the postovulatory temperatures are above the baseline. You'll also want to do a *cross check* between your BBT and CM. You can confirm ovulation once you've observed a sustained thermal shift — *and* you've observed a clear and obvious shift from mucus days to dry days.

What if my temperature rises slowly?

Different methods of FA charting have different rules for how to interpret temperatures. Some specify that the temperature must rise above a certain level in order to be valid, while others classify different types of temperature rises. However, the basic rules are the same no matter which method you use. You're looking for three temperatures that are higher than your normal preovulatory temperatures (specifically your previous six normal preovulatory temperatures). What I've found over the years is that temperature rises don't always look the same, but when you've ovulated you'll see a clear shift between your pre- and postovulatory temperatures. You'll easily be able to see three temperatures *in a row* that are higher than your previous six normal preovulatory temperatures. Even if the rise is "slow" and you don't experience a giant change from one day to the next, provided your temperature rises and stays high, you can confirm ovulation on the third consecutive day your temperatures are higher than they were before — provided your temperature shift matches up with your other fertile signs (CM and cervical position changes).

What if my temperature rises and then falls back the next day?

Since you're looking for three consecutive (normal) temperatures that are higher than your previous six (normal) preovulatory temperatures, if your temperature drops back down to the preovulatory range, then you must wait until you have three temperatures in a row that are all higher than the previous six to confirm a temperature shift. If your temperature rises and then falls back a bit the following day, it would still count as a temperature shift provided it doesn't fall below the baseline/coverline.

The key is having three *consecutive* high temperatures. Your temperature shift should be clear and obvious. The moment you feel confused, or you see that your temperatures are going back down into the preovulatory range, the simplest explanation is that you probably haven't ovulated yet.

Whether you're actively trying to conceive or you're using FA to avoid pregnancy, it's crucial to accurately identify ovulation, and the best way to do it is to wait until all signs match up to each other — and to the rules. Put simply, when in doubt, wait three days and you'll have your answer.

What if my temperatures are erratic and frequently swing between high and low on my chart?

The first thing I like to rule out is incorrect temperature taking. Review the instructions for correct temperature taking on page 10, and make sure you're keeping your thermometer in place for a full 10 minutes before turning it on. Many women find that by simply following the 10-minute rule their temperatures stabilize and their charts are much easier to interpret.

If you're already following the 10-minute rule and your temperatures are still erratic, it's time to do some detective work to figure out what else could be affecting your temps. My best advice is to start taking note of any actions you feel could be related to your erratic temperatures on your chart. Anything that triggers your immune system (illness, allergies, seasonal allergies, food sensitivities, immunizations or other injections, etc.) will likely affect your temperatures. Similarly, your temperatures may be sensitive to sleep disruptions and varying wake-up times, travel, and time zone differences; many women also experience dramatic fluctuations in temperature when they consume alcohol.

Regardless of these fluctuations, you should be able to see a clear and obvious shift once you ovulate. As you embark on your charting journey, you will rarely (if ever) have a "perfect" chart because you are a real woman (not a robot), and your cycles reflect the state of your overall health. As you learn which factors affect your temperatures and your charts, you'll gain a much deeper insight into how your body responds to everyday life. The purpose of charting isn't to have a perfect-looking cycle every month; instead, it is to develop body literacy and enter into a lifelong conversation with your body and your cycles.

How do I confirm pregnancy with my temperature?

When one of your eggs is fertilized and successfully implants into your endometrium, pregnancy occurs. During the early stages of pregnancy, your temperatures not only remain high, but they climb even higher than your normal postovulatory temperatures (when pregnancy does not occur, your corpus luteum stops producing progesterone, your temperatures fall back down to preovulatory levels, and you get your period about 12 to 14 days after ovulation). You can confirm pregnancy when you have 18 normal temperatures (in a row) that are higher than your previous six normal preovulatory temperatures. Many pregnant women notice what's called a *triphasic shift* — a second shift to higher temperatures once pregnancy has occurred — while other pregnant women simply notice a steady rise in their temperatures 12 to 14 days after ovulation.

Should I continue taking my temperature when I get pregnant?

Experience has taught me that continuing to take your temperature once you're pregnant isn't helpful and instead causes additional stress. Many (if not all) women are concerned in the early weeks of pregnancy that they might miscarry. It's true that in some cases, if your pregnancy is not viable, your temperatures will fail to continue rising. In other words, low BBTs during the first few weeks of pregnancy can be an early indication of a pending miscarriage. For this reason, many women continue taking their temperature for several weeks after pregnancy is confirmed. However, I don't advise you to do this, and here's why:

Your BBT will fluctuate from day to day, and when you see a temperature that is slightly higher or lower than you expected, it can (and will!) cause unnecessary stress. Taking your temperatures won't help you prevent miscarriage, and if you have any concerns about your pregnancy, you should talk to your doctor. When you see your 18th high temperature post ovulation (and you've taken a home pregnancy test and/or confirmed your pregnancy with your doctor via a blood test) you can put down your thermometer until you're ready to start charting again post pregnancy.

What if I can't make sense of my temperatures?

If you're sick for several days and your temperatures are all over the place, you're still looking for three normal temperatures that are higher than your previous six normal preovulatory temps. If your temperatures are questionable (due to the factors listed earlier in this section), wait until they stabilize.

Remember these two important steps:

1. When in doubt, wait three days until your observations start to make sense again, and
2. Rely on your CM observations in the meantime.

If you can't see a clear pattern between your low preovulatory temperatures and your high postovulatory temperatures, assume you haven't ovulated until your temperature pattern becomes clear and consistent. If you're ever unsure of your observations, consider yourself fertile until it all makes sense again —even if it takes several days! Head over to thefifthvitalsignbook.com/bonuses to access a free training video where I address a variety of common questions about BBT charting.

Charting Your Cervical Position

Cervical position is more of a secondary sign that works best in conjunction with CM and BBT. Tracking changes in your cervical position will give you more confidence in your observations by giving you an additional data point. If you've never checked your cervix before, or if you've always found your cervix confusing, I highly recommend that you commit to checking it every day for one full cycle.

Closed **Open**

The image above depicts the cervix in both an open and closed position.

Choose a time of day that makes sense for you, and try to stay consistent. Insert your middle finger into your vagina, touch your cervix, and notice what it feels like. If you're having a hard time finding your cervix, try squatting while you check, which can make it easier to reach (refer to page 17 for a full description of how to check your cervix). A disclaimer: not a whole lot changes until you approach ovulation. If your cervix were a newspaper, most days it would have nothing to report. But as you'd start approaching ovulation, you'd notice a buzz of news. The "breaking news" in your cervical newspaper is the shift that happens after ovulation — you'll notice a dramatic shift from high, soft, and open to low, firm, and closed. You'll also notice an abrupt change in the tilt of your cervix. Once you feel the shift, you'll have an additional fertile sign to help you identify your fertile window and confirm ovulation.

As you approach ovulation (during your fertile window), your cervix is higher inside your vagina, softer to the touch (like the softness of your lips), and you may feel a dimple indicating your cervix is open (*high, soft, and open*). After ovulation your cervix is lower inside your vagina, firm to the touch (like the firmness of your nose), closed, and tilted (*low, firm, closed, and tilted*). The image depicts the cervix in both an open and closed position.

Common Questions About Cervical Position Charting

Is it necessary to chart cervical position?

Cervical position is an *optional* sign that can be extremely helpful to corroborate your CM and BBT observations. Monitoring your cervical position gives you an additional tool to confirm ovulation and is especially beneficial in any cycle when your CM or BBT readings are unclear. I recommend cervical position charting in certain situations:

1. When your CM production is limited (with very little to no mucus production even though you are ovulating regularly), and
2. During any cycle when your CM and/or BBT observations are confusing (for example, if you have a yeast infection and you're having a difficult time identifying your fertile window, or if you're sick and have an elevated temperature before your sustained thermal shift). With that said, not all women are comfortable enough to insert their finger into their vagina and check their cervix. If that's you, not to worry — you can reliably use FA without cervical position charting — although it's a helpful additional sign to have at your fingertips (pun intended).

How do I check my cervix?

Wash your hands and insert your middle or index finger inside your vagina until you feel your cervix. Your cervix is located at the end of your vagina, and it feels similar to the end of your nose or your (puckered) lips. Choose a time of day and stick with it every day for one full cycle to help you get into the habit of checking. You may want to do your check when you're in the shower (given that you're already naked and your hands are clean!). When you check your cervix, you're feeling for four specific observations: *height, openness, firmness, and tilt*. Note how each aspect of your cervix changes as you check throughout your cycle.

How can I tell if my cervix is "high" or "low"?

Unlike your BBT, cervical position changes are subjective. Each woman will experience different cervical position changes, and no two women's cervixes will feel exactly the same. When your cervix is low, you'll notice that you don't have to insert your finger very far inside your vagina, and when it's high, you may have to insert your finger quite far inside (some women may not be able to feel their cervix when it's at its highest point). Check your cervix daily for one full cycle (every day from the last day of your period until the day before your next one begins), and this will help you identify whether your cervix is high, medium, or low.

How do I confirm ovulation by checking my cervix?

Unlike BBT and CM charting, cervical position is not a sign I would recommend using on its own. I suggest using it to confirm ovulation by cross-checking your cervical position with BBT and CM. As you approach ovulation (during your fertile window) your cervix rises to a higher position inside your vagina; it is typically soft, open, and facing downward. Once you ovulate, you'll feel a "dramatic" shift from soft, high, and open, to low, firm, closed, and tilted (usually backward). This shift typically happens from one day to the next and is often quite pronounced. When my clients commit to checking their cervix daily for one full cycle, they describe the postovulatory shift in cervical position as the most "exciting" event that happens throughout their entire cycle. Once you've felt the shift (from high, open, and soft to low, firm, closed, and tilted), *and* cross-checked it with your CM (you've gone from mucus to dry days) and BBT (you've had a sustained thermal shift), you can be confident that you have ovulated.

How does cervical position change after birth, miscarriage and/or abortion? Will the cervix ever be fully closed?

Prior to birth, miscarriage (depending on how far along you were), and/or an abortion, the "closed" position of your cervix will feel *fully* closed. Take a moment to touch your nose (go ahead … I'll wait). Your nose feels similar to your closed cervix before you've experienced pregnancy and/or birth. When your cervix is in an "open" position, it feels softer, and the openness feels somewhat like a dimple. Pucker your lips and touch them (yep ... still waiting for you to check it!). This is what your "open" cervix feels like prior to birth, miscarriage, and/or abortion.

Once you've given birth or experienced a miscarriage and/or an abortion, your cervix may never feel fully closed again. Your "closed" cervix will always be partially dilated when you touch it. You may feel a slight opening that's always there regardless of where you are in your cycle. When your cervix is in the "open" position it will feel softer and the opening will feel more pronounced compared to the "closed" position.

Even though your post-baby cervix will always be partially dilated, you can still reliably identify the change in your cervical position throughout your cycle. My advice is the same in this situation: check your cervix daily for one full cycle and note the changes in height, firmness, openness, and tilt. The goal is to identify how your cervix changes during your fertile window as you approach ovulation — not to try and fit into someone else's definition of how the cervix is "supposed" to feel. Even if your cervix is partially dilated throughout your cycle, you'll still be able to identify the way it changes as you pass through the different stages of your cycle.

What if my cervix is so high I can't reach it?

If you can't reach your cervix at certain times in your cycle, try squatting when you check it (as if you were playing a game of leapfrog), which may lower your cervix. You can also try lifting up one leg when you check. If you can feel your cervix at certain times of your cycle and not others, that may be one of the ways you identify the change in your cervical position. If you can't *ever* feel your cervix, either your uterus is in a position that prevents you from reaching it, or your fingers are too small. In that case, you may simply have to skip cervical position charting altogether. But if you're keen on adding cervical position checking to your routine, commit to checking it daily for one full cycle.

Does the angle or tilt of my cervix change throughout my cycle?

Yes, tilt is one of the lesser known aspects of cervical position charting. If you were to zoom the lens out and observe your entire uterus at different phases of your menstrual cycle, you'd notice that not only does your cervical position change, but the position of your uterus also changes. Your uterus sits in a flat position following menstruation (often causing the cervix to face backward), an upright position during your fertile window as you approach ovulation, and reverts back to the flat position once again after ovulation. The change in the tilt of your cervix always happens in conjunction with the other signs of ovulation (firmness, position, and openness).

For many women, identifying the change in the tilt of the cervix is the final piece of the puzzle that helps them make sense of their cervical position changes. It may explain why you can't always feel the opening when you check your cervix, as the opening may be facing backward (or to one side or the other) when you're not in your fertile window.

What if my cervix changes position throughout the day?

If you check your cervix multiple times per day, you may notice that it is in a different position at certain times. The cervix is the lower part of your uterus, and your uterus is a surprisingly dynamic organ. Not only does it change position and tilt as you pass through the different phases of your menstrual cycle and during sexual activity in response to sexual arousal, but your uterus may shift position throughout the day depending on your activity level or a number of other factors. For this reason, I recommend checking your cervix once (and only once!) per day. Checking it multiple times each day only adds to the confusion, so don't bother! Choose a specific time of day (mornings or evenings, for example) and stick with it over the course of at least one full cycle.

Charting Your Observations

Now it's time for the fun part — *charting your cycles!* Along with several defined spaces on each chart, a number of blank spaces allow you to customize your details (as shown below). These charting pages work with any sympto-thermal or mucus-only method of cycle tracking. They can be used with specific notations if you follow a particular charting method, or you can develop your own notations as you go. This workbook includes *three years* of charting pages (36 charts in total).

Like any new skill, it takes time and practice to gain full confidence using FA. Learning how to chart on your own through books or other solo resources takes anywhere from three to six full cycles of charting. You can speed up your learning curve by working with a qualified charting instructor. Consider seeking support if you plan to rely on FA as your primary birth control method or if you have any difficulties interpreting your charts. Refer to the resources section on page 112 for my top recommendations as you embark on your charting journey!

Cycle: ___ Month(s): ________ Year: ____ Length: ______ Luteal Phase: ______ Ovulation: ______

Cycle Day 1 2 3 4 5 6 7 8 9 10 11 12 13 14 15 16 17 18 19 20 21 22 23 24 25 26 27 28 29 30 31 32 33 34 35

Weekday

Date

Mucus Pattern

Sensation

Mucus Description

Sex

Cervical Position

Cycle Day 1 2 3 4 5 6 7 8 9 10 11 12 13 14 15 16 17 18 19 20 21 22 23 24 25 26 27 28 29 30 31 32 33 34 35

Time

Luteal Phase Count

Temperature

98°

97°

Daily Notes

1 ___
2 ___
3 ___
4 ___
5 ___
6 ___
7 ___
8 ___
9 ___
10 ___
11 ___
12 ___
13 ___
14 ___
15 ___
16 ___
17 ___
18 ___
19 ___
20 ___
21 ___
22 ___
23 ___
24 ___
25 ___
26 ___
27 ___
28 ___
29 ___
30 ___
31 ___
32 ___
33 ___
34 ___
35 ___

Blank Chart

I created the sample chart below to help you visualize your completed chart. I'll take you through each section and outline possible notations, but I know you'll develop your own shorthand over time. Visit thefifthvitalsignbook.com/workbookbonuses to access a free training video that takes you through several important tips for using this charting workbook. Join my private Facebook group (fertilityfriday.com/community) and show us how you've personalized your charts!

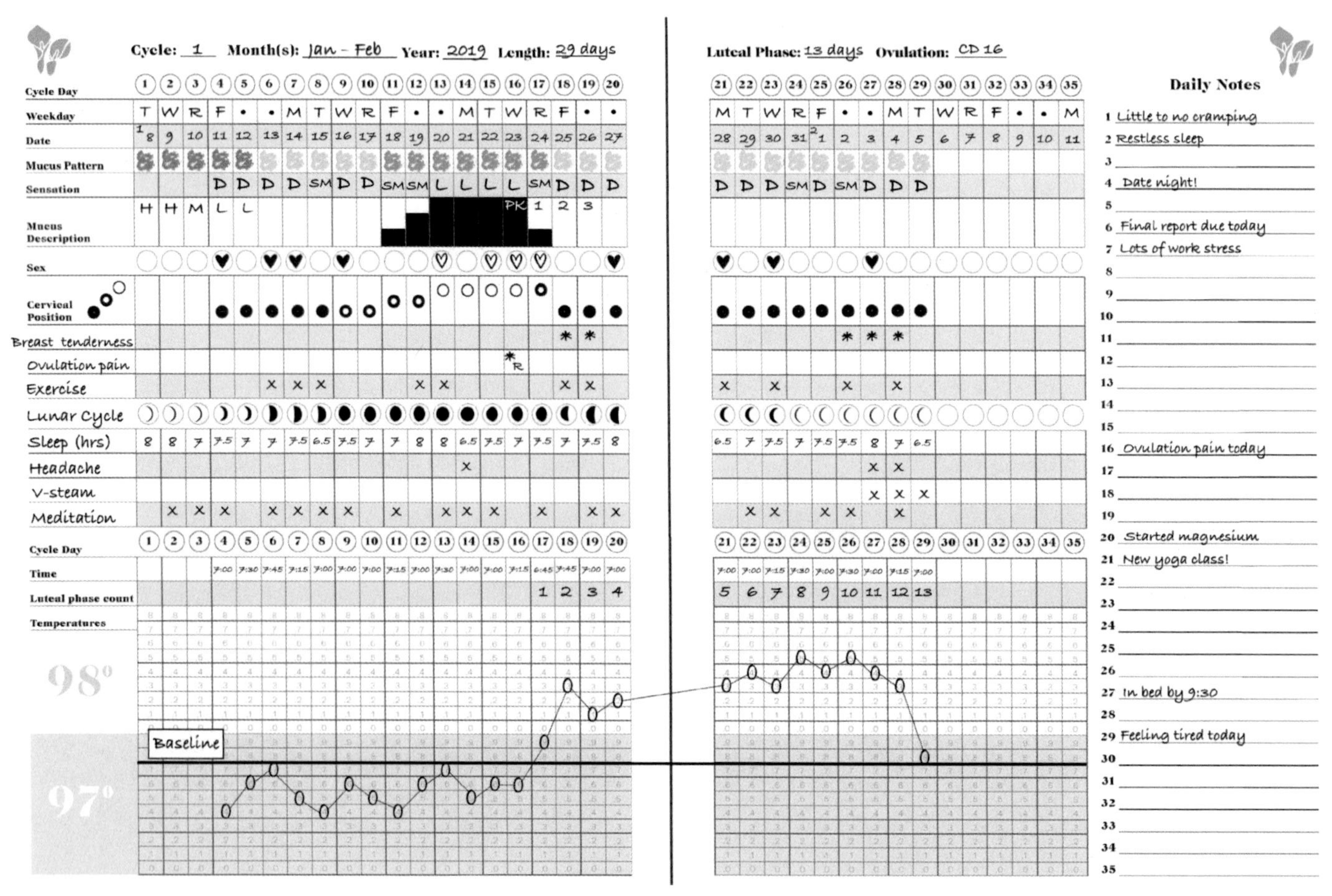

Sample Chart

Using the Charting Pages

Cycle Details

Cycle	Keep track of how many cycles you've charted.
Month(s)	Indicate which month(s) your current cycle falls into.
Year	Current year.
Length	Once your cycle has finished, note the total length here.
Luteal Phase	Once your cycle has finished, note the length of your postovulatory (luteal) phase here (see Chapter 4 of *The Fifth Vital Sign*).
Ovulation	Once you've confirmed ovulation, note the approximate date (based on the shift in your BBT and CM — shown as CD [cycle day] 16 on the sample chart).
Cycle Day	This section tracks which day of the cycle you're on and appears twice: at the top of each chart and in the temperature section.
Weekday	Note the day of the week by using these letters (or your own shorthand): **M** – Monday, **T** – Tuesday, **W** – Wednesday, **R** – Thursday, **F** – Friday, and dots (•) for Saturday and Sunday. Using dots for the weekend days visually defines the weekdays and weekends, and using "**R**" for Thursday avoids confusing it with Tuesday.
Date	Use this section to show the day of the month. I typically record the number of the month at the beginning of each month to help me keep track. On the sample chart, you'll see that I wrote "1/8" on cycle day 1 to indicate January 8th and "2/1" on cycle day 25 to indicate February 1st.

Mucus and Cervical Position

Mucus Pattern	Record your dry days, mucus days, and any days of bleeding in this row using dots, circles, or simply filling in the squares. You can use pencil crayons, markers, coloured pens, or highlighters. Choose a different colour for dry days, mucus days, and menstruation. In the sample chart I use these colours: **Light Green** = dry days, **Blue** = mucus days, and **Pink** = menstruation and/or mid-cycle bleeding/spotting. Note: **PK** = peak day, and the numbers shown (1, 2, 3) indicate the fertile period that follows.
Sensation	Note here the most "fertile" sensation you feel each day when you wipe. Choose a notation for Dry, Smooth, and Lubricative. In the sample chart I used these notations: **D** – Dry, **SM** – Smooth, and **L** – Lubricative.
Mucus Description	In this section, note your most "fertile" CM observation each day by either colouring in the box to illustrate the quality and quantity of your mucus (as shown in the sample chart) or using notations such as **E** – Eggwhite, **C** – Creamy, **S** – Sticky, or **W** – Wet. If you follow a specific charting system, you can add your notations here, or you may wish to develop your own shorthand. Also use this section to note your menstrual flow: **H** – Heavy, **M** – Moderate, **L** – Light, or **VL** – Very Light.
Sex	Record here when you have sex and whether it was protected or unprotected. You may want to use hearts (as shown in the sample chart). Filled in hearts = unprotected sex and blank hearts = protected sex. You may also want to use different notations such as: **I** – Intercourse (unprotected), **i** – intercourse (protected), **W** – Withdrawal, **a** – Alternative sex, or use your own shorthand.
Cervical Position	Use this section to track cervical position changes. Indicate changes in the firmness, openness, position, and tilt of your cervix by drawing circles (or using your own shorthand). Draw a filled-in circle at the bottom of the box to indicate low, firm, and closed or draw a blank circle at the top of the box to indicate high, soft, and open (as shown in the sample chart).
Blank Spaces	The following eight rows are left blank intentionally to allow you to record your own observations. In the sample chart I've included *breast tenderness, ovulation pain, exercise, lunar cycle, sleep (number of hours), headache, V-steam (vaginal steam), and meditation,* but you can include anything you wish. Other possible options include mid-cycle spotting, abnormal bleeding, pregnancy and/or OPK testing, disturbed/interrupted sleep, vitamins or supplements you're taking, dietary and/or lifestyle changes you've made, personal situations, school or work related activities, and anything in between.

Temperature

Time	Indicate what time you took your temperature upon waking.
Luteal Phase Count	Note the length of your postovulatory (luteal) phase, starting the count on day 1 of your sustained thermal shift (cycle day 17 on the sample chart).
Temperature	Record your daily temperature readings in Fahrenheit. The range provided goes from 97.0 to 98.8°F. Round your temperature readings up or down accordingly (0.05 and higher round up, 0.04 and lower round down), and circle the appropriate temperature on the chart. You can connect the dots by drawing lines between your temperatures. Use a ruler to draw the baseline *after* you've confirmed ovulation with your thermal shift. As shown in the sample chart, the baseline divides your pre- and postovulatory temperatures; it is drawn slightly above your highest (normal) preovulatory temperature (based on the previous six — see page 13 and Chapter 10 of *The Fifth Vital Sign*).
Daily Notes	Use this section to record additional notes and observations that don't fit neatly on your charts. Each line corresponds to your current cycle day. Anything goes in this section. Review the sample chart for ideas of what you might write in this section.

Using the Cycle Summary Pages

Cycle Summary Pages

Year at a Glance	These calendar blocks are left blank intentionally to allow you to use them based on the current year. Note the month and year, and add in the current dates.
Cycle Monitoring	Note your cycle details here (such as total length, luteal phase length, and estimated ovulation date) for an annual snapshot of your charts.

Cycle Details

Cycle #	Keep track of how many cycles you've charted by entering the cycle number.
Start Date	Note the date your cycle began.
End Date	Note the date your cycle ended.
Length	Record the total length of your cycle here.
Luteal Phase	Note the length of your luteal phase.
Ovulation	Note the approximate date of ovulation.
Average Cycle Length	Once you have completed 12 cycles, calculate the average and enter it here.
Average Luteal Phase	Once you have completed 12 cycles, calculate the average luteal phase length and enter it here.

Cycle Summary Pages

Year at a Glance

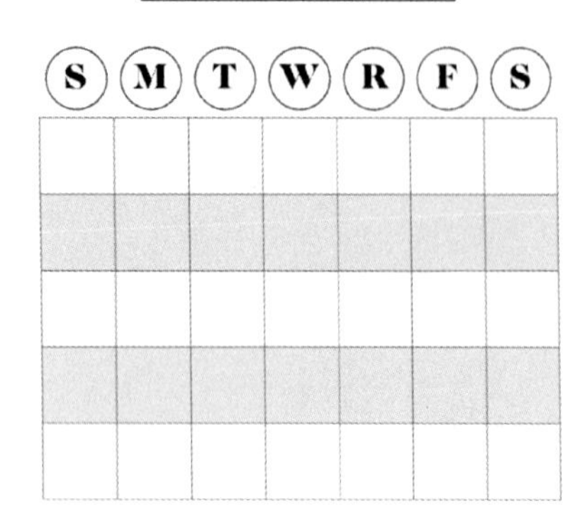

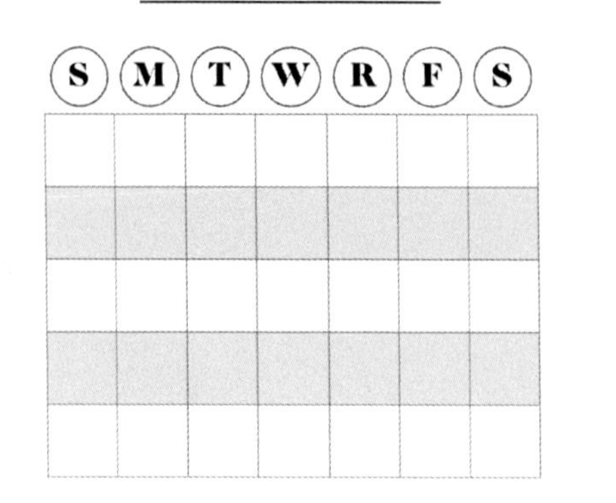

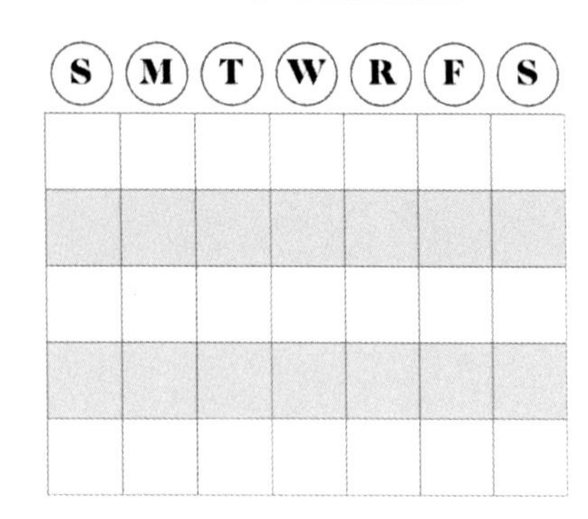

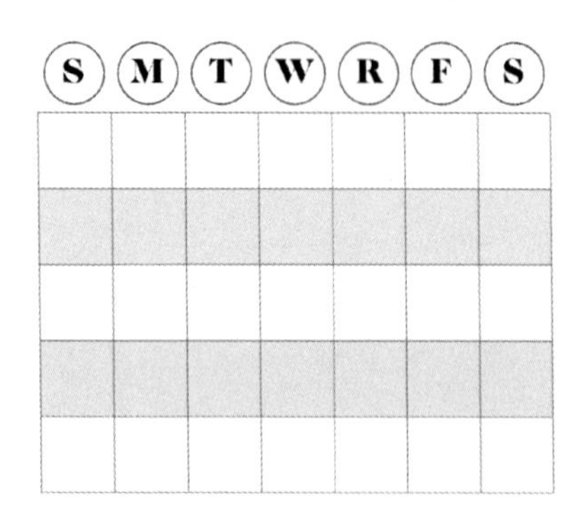

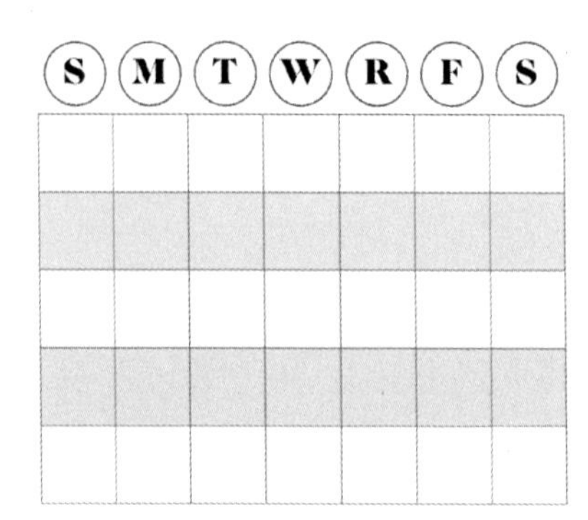

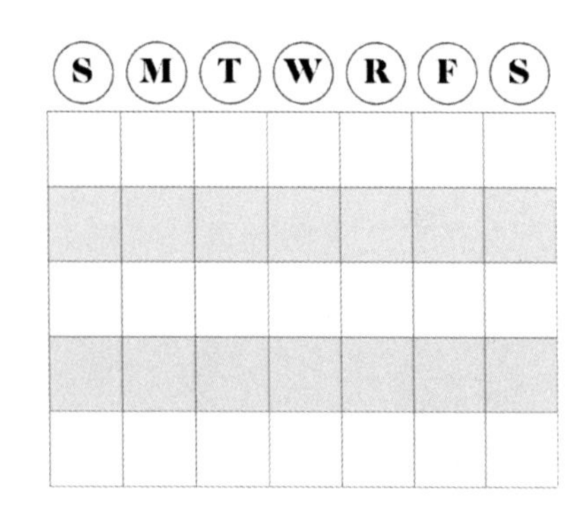

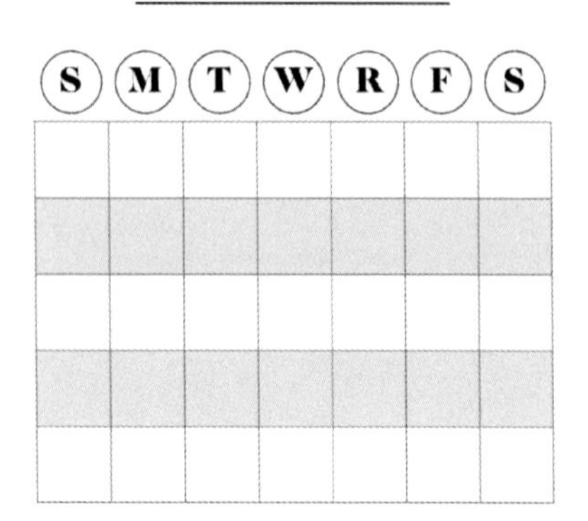

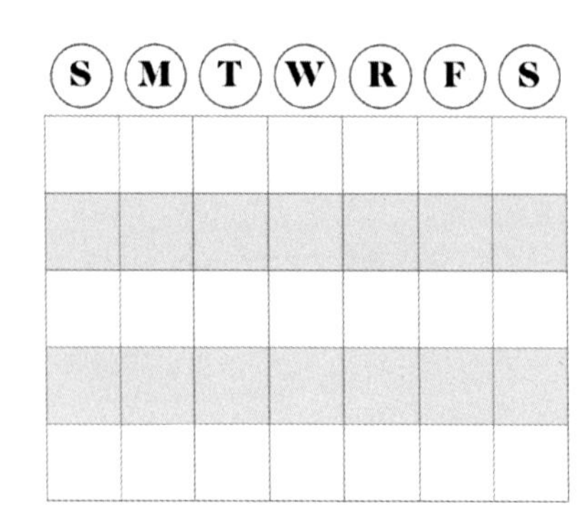

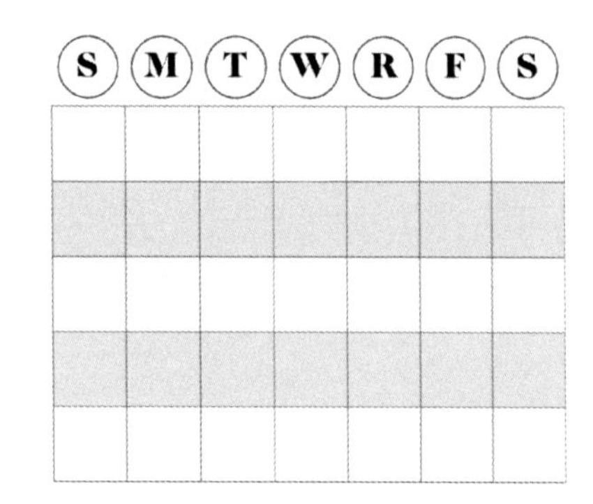

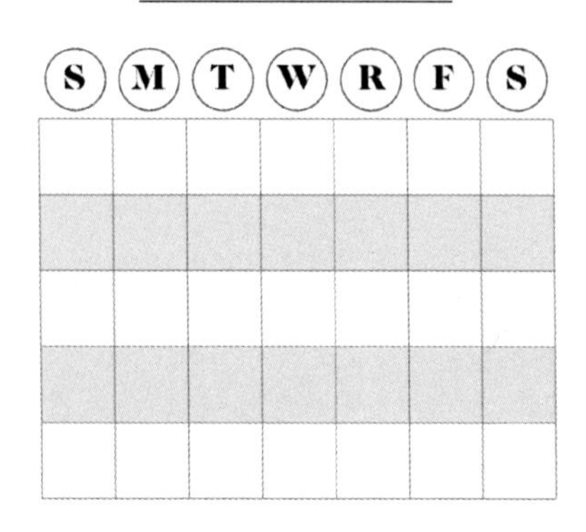

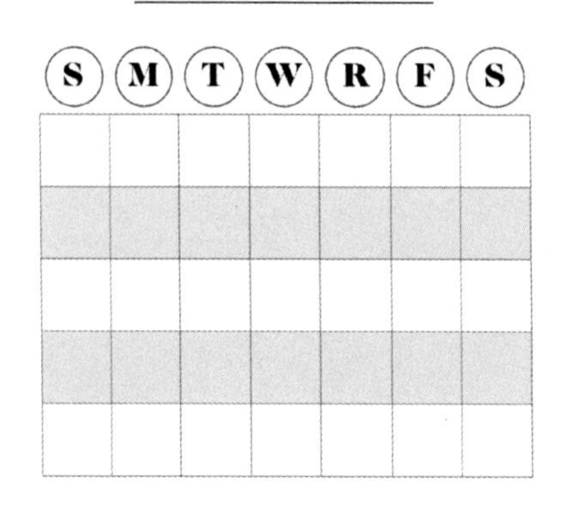

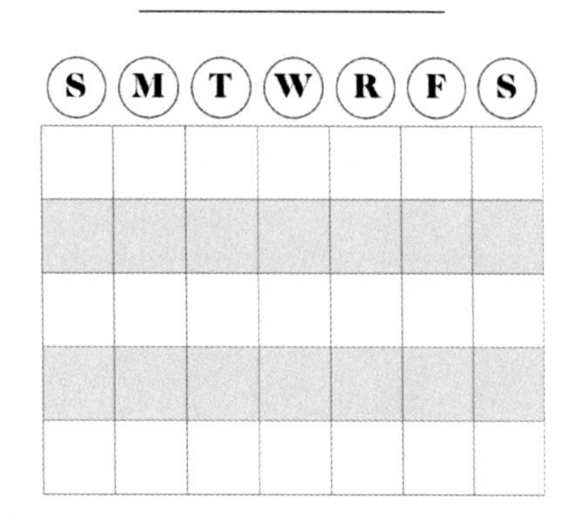

Cycle Monitoring

Cycle #	Start Date	End Date	Length	Luteal Phase	Ovulation

Average Cycle Length ______________________________

Average Luteal Phase Length ______________________________

Notes ______________________________

Year at a Glance

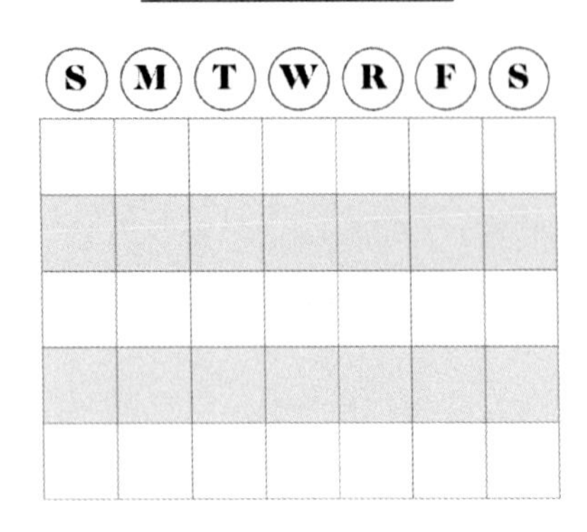

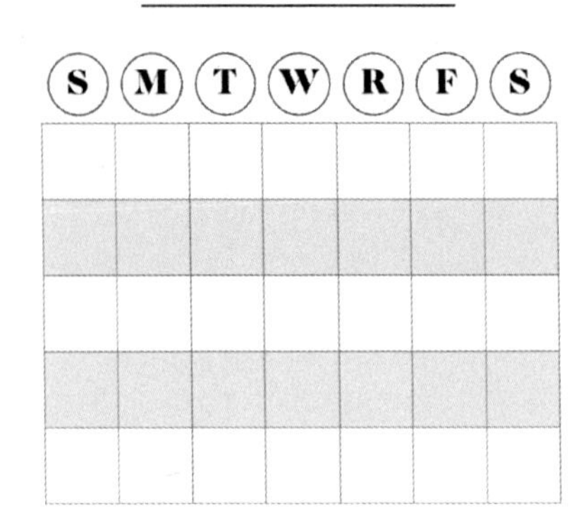

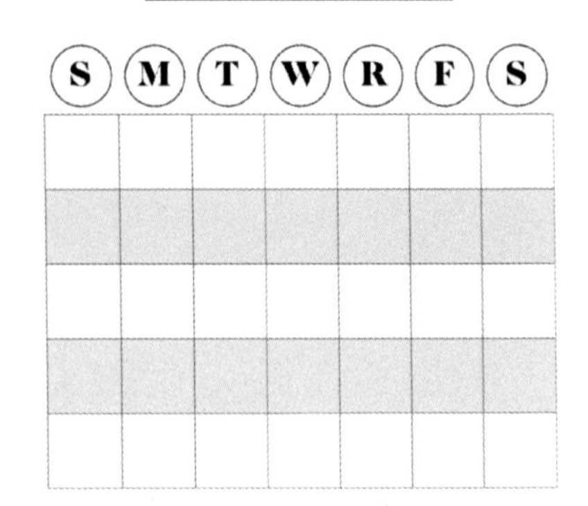

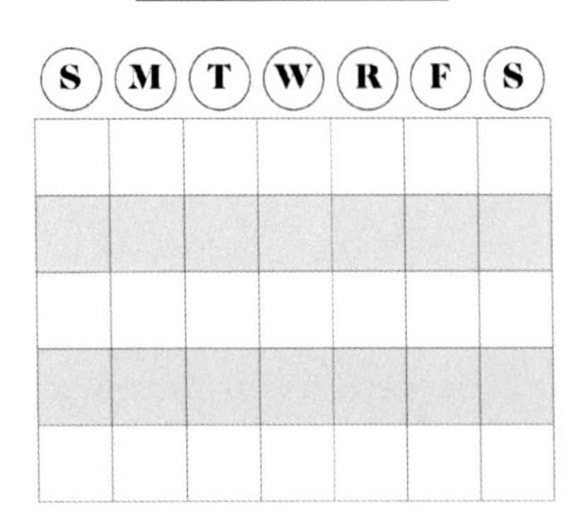

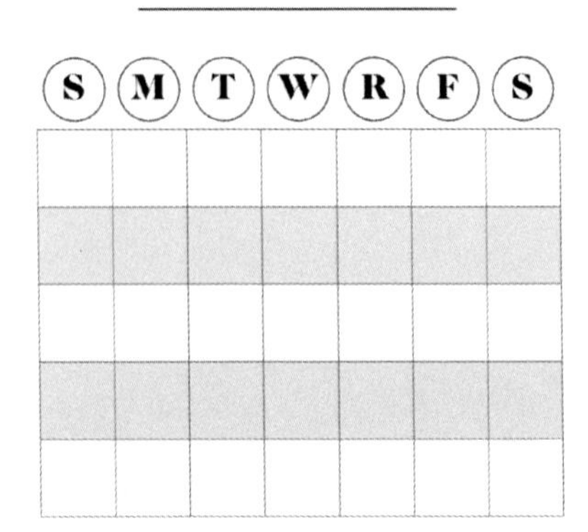

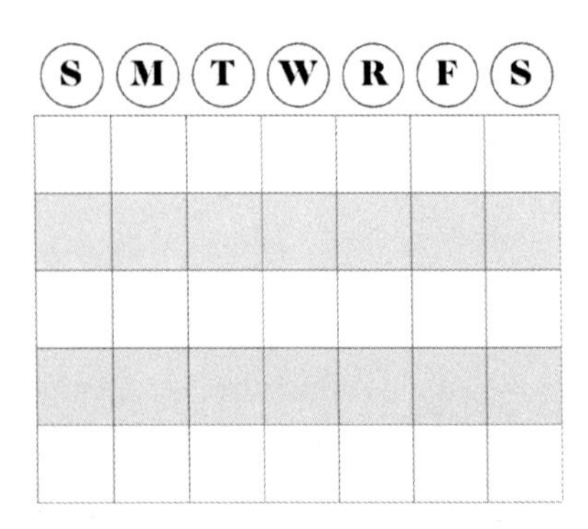

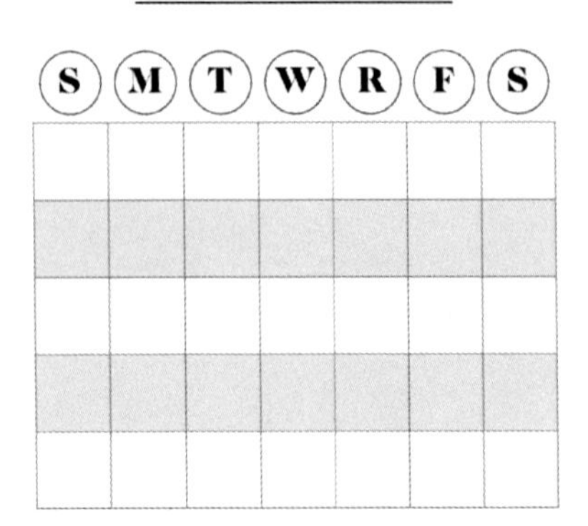

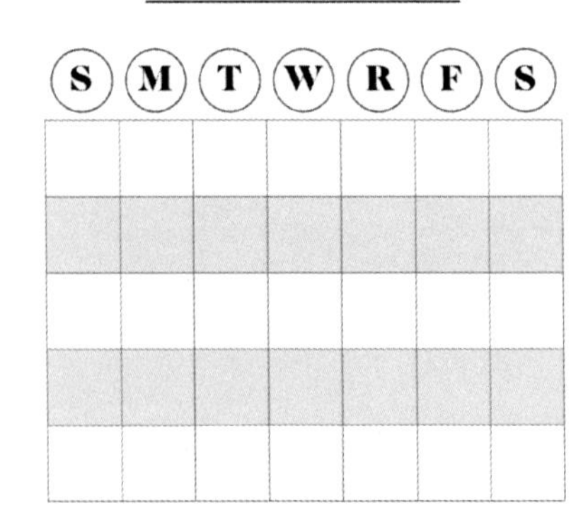

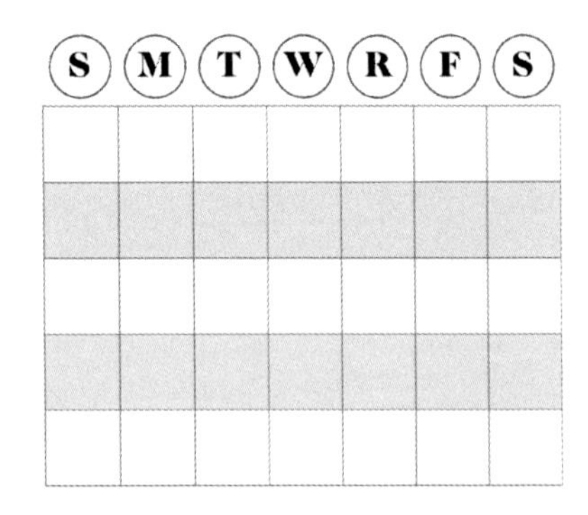

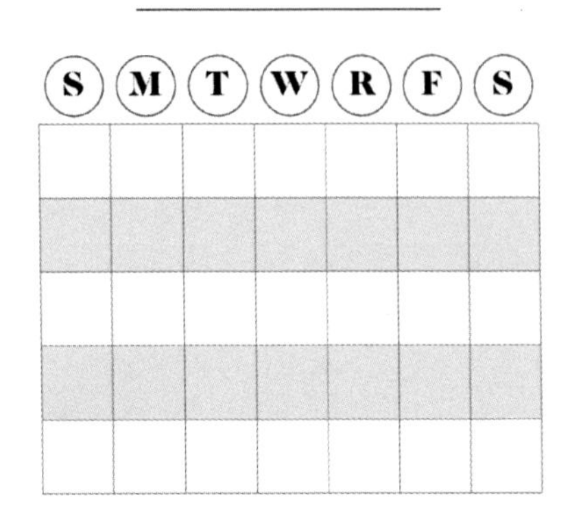

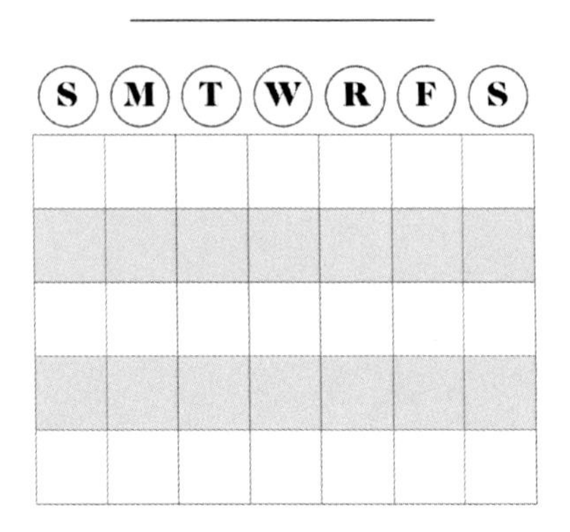

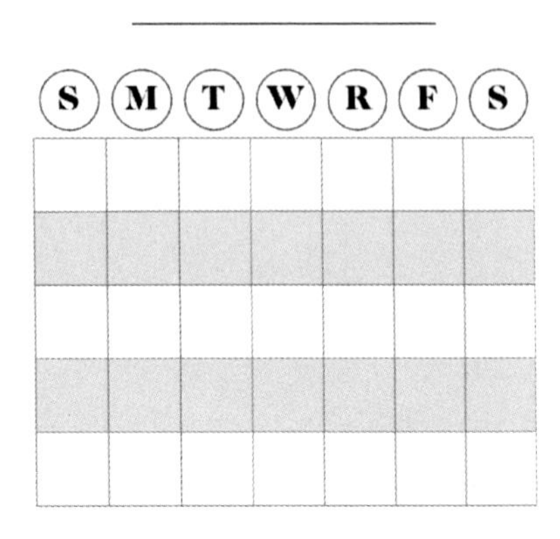

Cycle Monitoring

Cycle #	Start Date	End Date	Length	Luteal Phase	Ovulation

Average Cycle Length ______________________

Average Luteal Phase Length ______________________

Notes ______________________

Year at a Glance

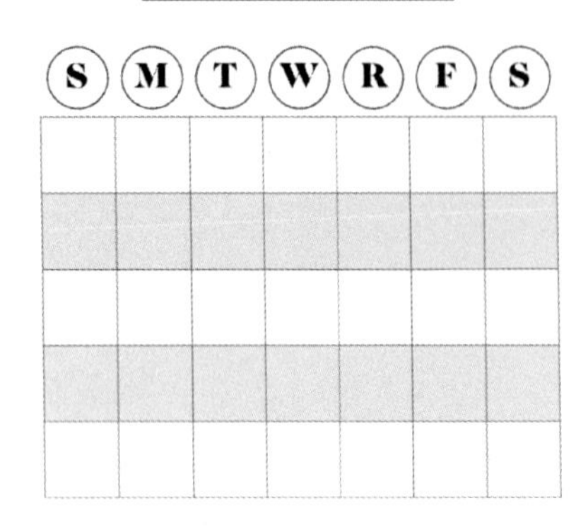

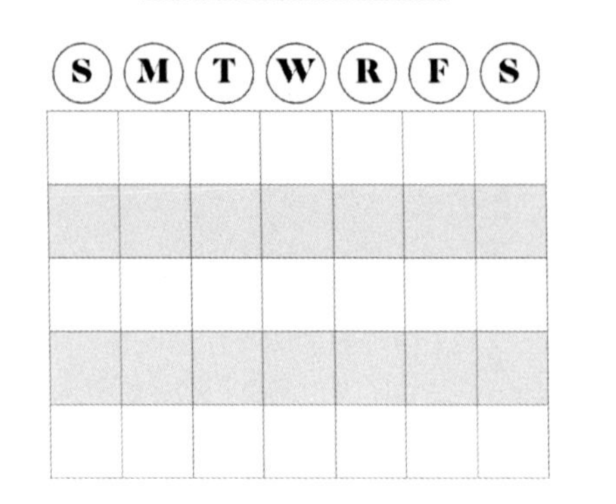

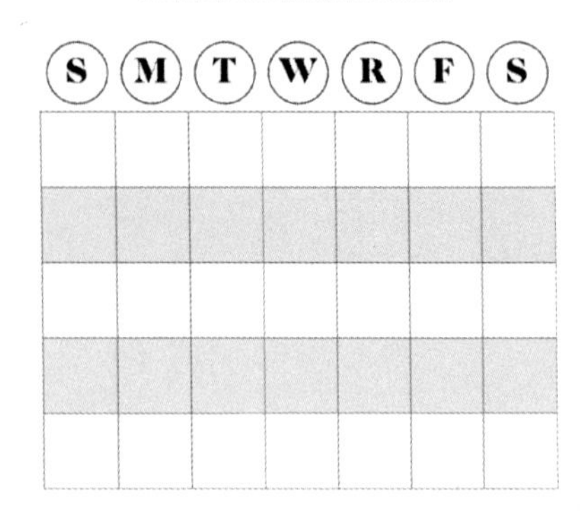

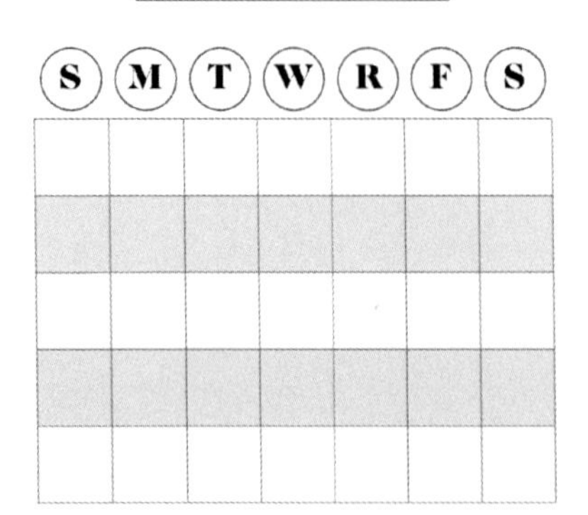

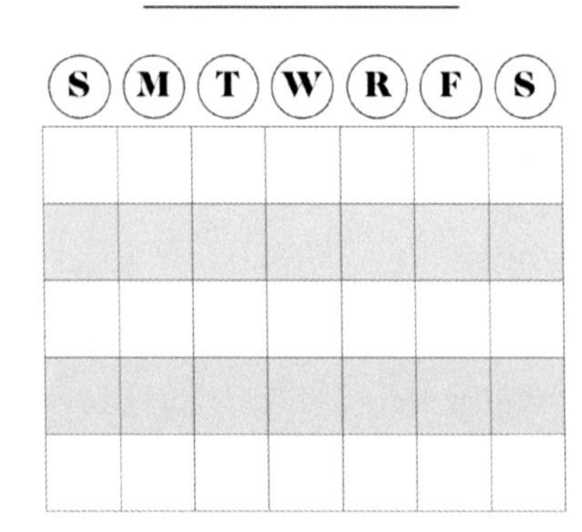

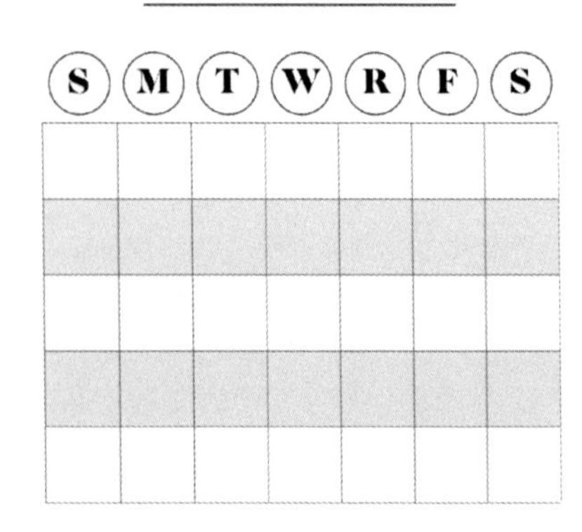

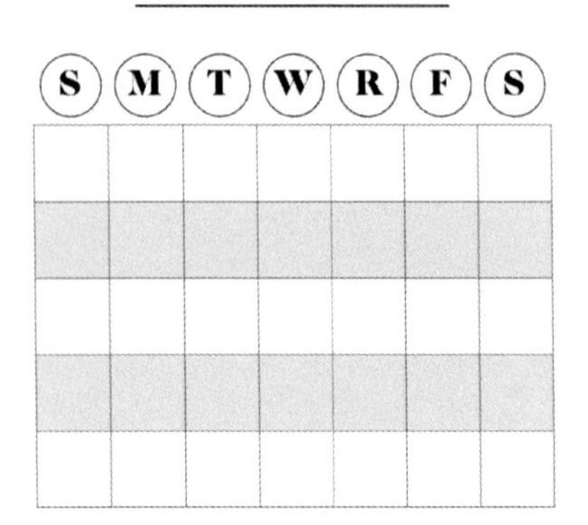

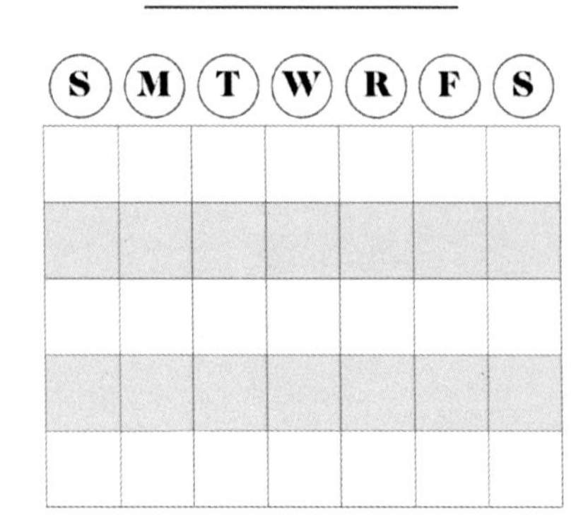

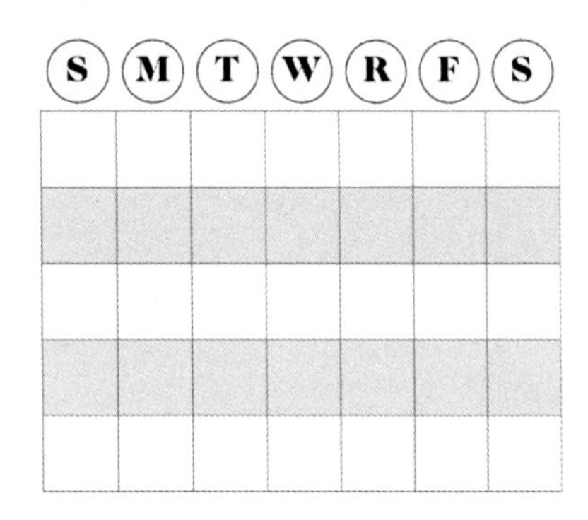

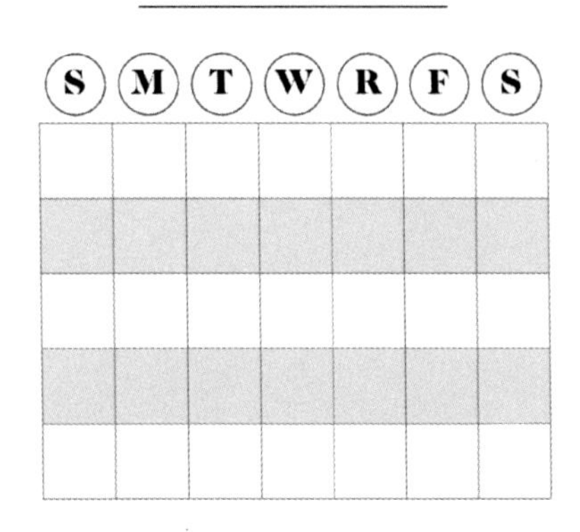

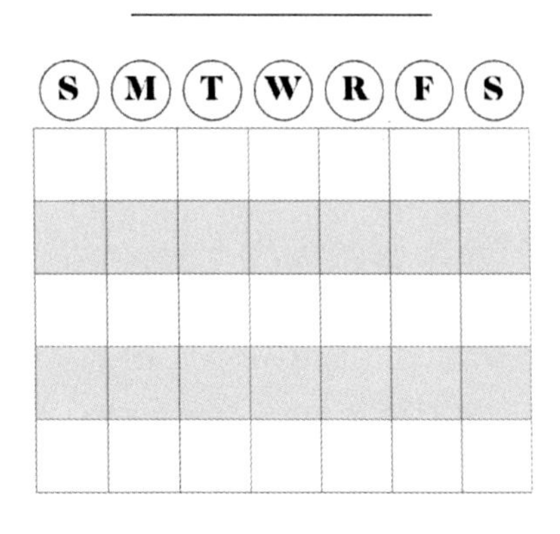

Cycle Monitoring

Cycle #	Start Date	End Date	Length	Luteal Phase	Ovulation

Average Cycle Length ______________________

Average Luteal Phase Length ______________________

Notes ______________________

Reflections

Reflections

Reflections

Charting Pages

Cycle: ____ **Month(s):** ____________ **Year:** ______ **Length:** _________

Cycle Day	1	2	3	4	5	6	7	8	9	10	11	12	13	14	15	16	17	18	19	20
Weekday																				
Date																				
Mucus Pattern																				
Sensation																				
Mucus Description																				
Sex																				
Cervical Position																				

Cycle Day	1	2	3	4	5	6	7	8	9	10	11	12	13	14	15	16	17	18	19	20
Time																				
Luteal Phase Count																				
Temperature	.8	.8	.8	.8	.8	.8	.8	.8	.8	.8	.8	.8	.8	.8	.8	.8	.8	.8	.8	.8
	.7	.7	.7	.7	.7	.7	.7	.7	.7	.7	.7	.7	.7	.7	.7	.7	.7	.7	.7	.7
	.6	.6	.6	.6	.6	.6	.6	.6	.6	.6	.6	.6	.6	.6	.6	.6	.6	.6	.6	.6
	.5	.5	.5	.5	.5	.5	.5	.5	.5	.5	.5	.5	.5	.5	.5	.5	.5	.5	.5	.5
98°	.4	.4	.4	.4	.4	.4	.4	.4	.4	.4	.4	.4	.4	.4	.4	.4	.4	.4	.4	.4
	.3	.3	.3	.3	.3	.3	.3	.3	.3	.3	.3	.3	.3	.3	.3	.3	.3	.3	.3	.3
	.2	.2	.2	.2	.2	.2	.2	.2	.2	.2	.2	.2	.2	.2	.2	.2	.2	.2	.2	.2
	.1	.1	.1	.1	.1	.1	.1	.1	.1	.1	.1	.1	.1	.1	.1	.1	.1	.1	.1	.1
	.0	.0	.0	.0	.0	.0	.0	.0	.0	.0	.0	.0	.0	.0	.0	.0	.0	.0	.0	.0
	.9	.9	.9	.9	.9	.9	.9	.9	.9	.9	.9	.9	.9	.9	.9	.9	.9	.9	.9	.9
	.8	.8	.8	.8	.8	.8	.8	.8	.8	.8	.8	.8	.8	.8	.8	.8	.8	.8	.8	.8
	.7	.7	.7	.7	.7	.7	.7	.7	.7	.7	.7	.7	.7	.7	.7	.7	.7	.7	.7	.7
	.6	.6	.6	.6	.6	.6	.6	.6	.6	.6	.6	.6	.6	.6	.6	.6	.6	.6	.6	.6
97°	.5	.5	.5	.5	.5	.5	.5	.5	.5	.5	.5	.5	.5	.5	.5	.5	.5	.5	.5	.5
	.4	.4	.4	.4	.4	.4	.4	.4	.4	.4	.4	.4	.4	.4	.4	.4	.4	.4	.4	.4
	.3	.3	.3	.3	.3	.3	.3	.3	.3	.3	.3	.3	.3	.3	.3	.3	.3	.3	.3	.3
	.2	.2	.2	.2	.2	.2	.2	.2	.2	.2	.2	.2	.2	.2	.2	.2	.2	.2	.2	.2
	.1	.1	.1	.1	.1	.1	.1	.1	.1	.1	.1	.1	.1	.1	.1	.1	.1	.1	.1	.1
	.0	.0	.0	.0	.0	.0	.0	.0	.0	.0	.0	.0	.0	.0	.0	.0	.0	.0	.0	.0

Luteal Phase: ________ **Ovulation:** __________

21	22	23	24	25	26	27	28	29	30	31	32	33	34	35

21	22	23	24	25	26	27	28	29	30	31	32	33	34	35
.8	.8	.8	.8	.8	.8	.8	.8	.8	.8	.8	.8	.8	.8	.8
.7	.7	.7	.7	.7	.7	.7	.7	.7	.7	.7	.7	.7	.7	.7
.6	.6	.6	.6	.6	.6	.6	.6	.6	.6	.6	.6	.6	.6	.6
.5	.5	.5	.5	.5	.5	.5	.5	.5	.5	.5	.5	.5	.5	.5
.4	.4	.4	.4	.4	.4	.4	.4	.4	.4	.4	.4	.4	.4	.4
.3	.3	.3	.3	.3	.3	.3	.3	.3	.3	.3	.3	.3	.3	.3
.2	.2	.2	.2	.2	.2	.2	.2	.2	.2	.2	.2	.2	.2	.2
.1	.1	.1	.1	.1	.1	.1	.1	.1	.1	.1	.1	.1	.1	.1
.0	.0	.0	.0	.0	.0	.0	.0	.0	.0	.0	.0	.0	.0	.0
.9	.9	.9	.9	.9	.9	.9	.9	.9	.9	.9	.9	.9	.9	.9
.8	.8	.8	.8	.8	.8	.8	.8	.8	.8	.8	.8	.8	.8	.8
.7	.7	.7	.7	.7	.7	.7	.7	.7	.7	.7	.7	.7	.7	.7
.6	.6	.6	.6	.6	.6	.6	.6	.6	.6	.6	.6	.6	.6	.6
.5	.5	.5	.5	.5	.5	.5	.5	.5	.5	.5	.5	.5	.5	.5
.4	.4	.4	.4	.4	.4	.4	.4	.4	.4	.4	.4	.4	.4	.4
.3	.3	.3	.3	.3	.3	.3	.3	.3	.3	.3	.3	.3	.3	.3
.2	.2	.2	.2	.2	.2	.2	.2	.2	.2	.2	.2	.2	.2	.2
.1	.1	.1	.1	.1	.1	.1	.1	.1	.1	.1	.1	.1	.1	.1
.0	.0	.0	.0	.0	.0	.0	.0	.0	.0	.0	.0	.0	.0	.0

Daily Notes

1 ____
2 ____
3 ____
4 ____
5 ____
6 ____
7 ____
8 ____
9 ____
10 ____
11 ____
12 ____
13 ____
14 ____
15 ____
16 ____
17 ____
18 ____
19 ____
20 ____
21 ____
22 ____
23 ____
24 ____
25 ____
26 ____
27 ____
28 ____
29 ____
30 ____
31 ____
32 ____
33 ____
34 ____
35 ____

Cycle: ____ Month(s): ____________ Year: ______ Length: _________

Cycle Day	1	2	3	4	5	6	7	8	9	10	11	12	13	14	15	16	17	18	19	20
Weekday																				
Date																				
Mucus Pattern																				
Sensation																				
Mucus Description																				
Sex	○	○	○	○	○	○	○	○	○	○	○	○	○	○	○	○	○	○	○	○
Cervical Position																				
	○	○	○	○	○	○	○	○	○	○	○	○	○	○	○	○	○	○	○	○

Cycle Day	1	2	3	4	5	6	7	8	9	10	11	12	13	14	15	16	17	18	19	20
Time																				
Luteal Phase Count																				
Temperature	.8	.8	.8	.8	.8	.8	.8	.8	.8	.8	.8	.8	.8	.8	.8	.8	.8	.8	.8	.8
	.7	.7	.7	.7	.7	.7	.7	.7	.7	.7	.7	.7	.7	.7	.7	.7	.7	.7	.7	.7
	.6	.6	.6	.6	.6	.6	.6	.6	.6	.6	.6	.6	.6	.6	.6	.6	.6	.6	.6	.6
	.5	.5	.5	.5	.5	.5	.5	.5	.5	.5	.5	.5	.5	.5	.5	.5	.5	.5	.5	.5
98°	.4	.4	.4	.4	.4	.4	.4	.4	.4	.4	.4	.4	.4	.4	.4	.4	.4	.4	.4	.4
	.3	.3	.3	.3	.3	.3	.3	.3	.3	.3	.3	.3	.3	.3	.3	.3	.3	.3	.3	.3
	.2	.2	.2	.2	.2	.2	.2	.2	.2	.2	.2	.2	.2	.2	.2	.2	.2	.2	.2	.2
	.1	.1	.1	.1	.1	.1	.1	.1	.1	.1	.1	.1	.1	.1	.1	.1	.1	.1	.1	.1
	.0	.0	.0	.0	.0	.0	.0	.0	.0	.0	.0	.0	.0	.0	.0	.0	.0	.0	.0	.0
	.9	.9	.9	.9	.9	.9	.9	.9	.9	.9	.9	.9	.9	.9	.9	.9	.9	.9	.9	.9
	.8	.8	.8	.8	.8	.8	.8	.8	.8	.8	.8	.8	.8	.8	.8	.8	.8	.8	.8	.8
	.7	.7	.7	.7	.7	.7	.7	.7	.7	.7	.7	.7	.7	.7	.7	.7	.7	.7	.7	.7
	.6	.6	.6	.6	.6	.6	.6	.6	.6	.6	.6	.6	.6	.6	.6	.6	.6	.6	.6	.6
97°	.5	.5	.5	.5	.5	.5	.5	.5	.5	.5	.5	.5	.5	.5	.5	.5	.5	.5	.5	.5
	.4	.4	.4	.4	.4	.4	.4	.4	.4	.4	.4	.4	.4	.4	.4	.4	.4	.4	.4	.4
	.3	.3	.3	.3	.3	.3	.3	.3	.3	.3	.3	.3	.3	.3	.3	.3	.3	.3	.3	.3
	.2	.2	.2	.2	.2	.2	.2	.2	.2	.2	.2	.2	.2	.2	.2	.2	.2	.2	.2	.2
	.1	.1	.1	.1	.1	.1	.1	.1	.1	.1	.1	.1	.1	.1	.1	.1	.1	.1	.1	.1
	.0	.0	.0	.0	.0	.0	.0	.0	.0	.0	.0	.0	.0	.0	.0	.0	.0	.0	.0	.0

Luteal Phase: ________ **Ovulation:** __________

21	22	23	24	25	26	27	28	29	30	31	32	33	34	35

21	22	23	24	25	26	27	28	29	30	31	32	33	34	35
.8	.8	.8	.8	.8	.8	.8	.8	.8	.8	.8	.8	.8	.8	.8
.7	.7	.7	.7	.7	.7	.7	.7	.7	.7	.7	.7	.7	.7	.7
.6	.6	.6	.6	.6	.6	.6	.6	.6	.6	.6	.6	.6	.6	.6
.5	.5	.5	.5	.5	.5	.5	.5	.5	.5	.5	.5	.5	.5	.5
.4	.4	.4	.4	.4	.4	.4	.4	.4	.4	.4	.4	.4	.4	.4
.3	.3	.3	.3	.3	.3	.3	.3	.3	.3	.3	.3	.3	.3	.3
.2	.2	.2	.2	.2	.2	.2	.2	.2	.2	.2	.2	.2	.2	.2
.1	.1	.1	.1	.1	.1	.1	.1	.1	.1	.1	.1	.1	.1	.1
.0	.0	.0	.0	.0	.0	.0	.0	.0	.0	.0	.0	.0	.0	.0
.9	.9	.9	.9	.9	.9	.9	.9	.9	.9	.9	.9	.9	.9	.9
.8	.8	.8	.8	.8	.8	.8	.8	.8	.8	.8	.8	.8	.8	.8
.7	.7	.7	.7	.7	.7	.7	.7	.7	.7	.7	.7	.7	.7	.7
.6	.6	.6	.6	.6	.6	.6	.6	.6	.6	.6	.6	.6	.6	.6
.5	.5	.5	.5	.5	.5	.5	.5	.5	.5	.5	.5	.5	.5	.5
.4	.4	.4	.4	.4	.4	.4	.4	.4	.4	.4	.4	.4	.4	.4
.3	.3	.3	.3	.3	.3	.3	.3	.3	.3	.3	.3	.3	.3	.3
.2	.2	.2	.2	.2	.2	.2	.2	.2	.2	.2	.2	.2	.2	.2
.1	.1	.1	.1	.1	.1	.1	.1	.1	.1	.1	.1	.1	.1	.1
.0	.0	.0	.0	.0	.0	.0	.0	.0	.0	.0	.0	.0	.0	.0

Daily Notes

1 ____
2 ____
3 ____
4 ____
5 ____
6 ____
7 ____
8 ____
9 ____
10 ____
11 ____
12 ____
13 ____
14 ____
15 ____
16 ____
17 ____
18 ____
19 ____
20 ____
21 ____
22 ____
23 ____
24 ____
25 ____
26 ____
27 ____
28 ____
29 ____
30 ____
31 ____
32 ____
33 ____
34 ____
35 ____

Cycle: ___ Month(s): ___________ Year: ______ Length: ________

Cycle Day	1	2	3	4	5	6	7	8	9	10	11	12	13	14	15	16	17	18	19	20
Weekday																				
Date																				
Mucus Pattern																				
Sensation																				
Mucus Description																				
Sex	○	○	○	○	○	○	○	○	○	○	○	○	○	○	○	○	○	○	○	○
Cervical Position																				
	○	○	○	○	○	○	○	○	○	○	○	○	○	○	○	○	○	○	○	○

Cycle Day	1	2	3	4	5	6	7	8	9	10	11	12	13	14	15	16	17	18	19	20
Time																				
Luteal Phase Count																				
Temperature	.8	.8	.8	.8	.8	.8	.8	.8	.8	.8	.8	.8	.8	.8	.8	.8	.8	.8	.8	.8
	.7	.7	.7	.7	.7	.7	.7	.7	.7	.7	.7	.7	.7	.7	.7	.7	.7	.7	.7	.7
	.6	.6	.6	.6	.6	.6	.6	.6	.6	.6	.6	.6	.6	.6	.6	.6	.6	.6	.6	.6
	.5	.5	.5	.5	.5	.5	.5	.5	.5	.5	.5	.5	.5	.5	.5	.5	.5	.5	.5	.5
98°	.4	.4	.4	.4	.4	.4	.4	.4	.4	.4	.4	.4	.4	.4	.4	.4	.4	.4	.4	.4
	.3	.3	.3	.3	.3	.3	.3	.3	.3	.3	.3	.3	.3	.3	.3	.3	.3	.3	.3	.3
	.2	.2	.2	.2	.2	.2	.2	.2	.2	.2	.2	.2	.2	.2	.2	.2	.2	.2	.2	.2
	.1	.1	.1	.1	.1	.1	.1	.1	.1	.1	.1	.1	.1	.1	.1	.1	.1	.1	.1	.1
	.0	.0	.0	.0	.0	.0	.0	.0	.0	.0	.0	.0	.0	.0	.0	.0	.0	.0	.0	.0
	.9	.9	.9	.9	.9	.9	.9	.9	.9	.9	.9	.9	.9	.9	.9	.9	.9	.9	.9	.9
	.8	.8	.8	.8	.8	.8	.8	.8	.8	.8	.8	.8	.8	.8	.8	.8	.8	.8	.8	.8
	.7	.7	.7	.7	.7	.7	.7	.7	.7	.7	.7	.7	.7	.7	.7	.7	.7	.7	.7	.7
	.6	.6	.6	.6	.6	.6	.6	.6	.6	.6	.6	.6	.6	.6	.6	.6	.6	.6	.6	.6
97°	.5	.5	.5	.5	.5	.5	.5	.5	.5	.5	.5	.5	.5	.5	.5	.5	.5	.5	.5	.5
	.4	.4	.4	.4	.4	.4	.4	.4	.4	.4	.4	.4	.4	.4	.4	.4	.4	.4	.4	.4
	.3	.3	.3	.3	.3	.3	.3	.3	.3	.3	.3	.3	.3	.3	.3	.3	.3	.3	.3	.3
	.2	.2	.2	.2	.2	.2	.2	.2	.2	.2	.2	.2	.2	.2	.2	.2	.2	.2	.2	.2
	.1	.1	.1	.1	.1	.1	.1	.1	.1	.1	.1	.1	.1	.1	.1	.1	.1	.1	.1	.1
	.0	.0	.0	.0	.0	.0	.0	.0	.0	.0	.0	.0	.0	.0	.0	.0	.0	.0	.0	.0

Luteal Phase: ________ **Ovulation:** ________

21 22 23 24 25 26 27 28 29 30 31 32 33 34 35

21	22	23	24	25	26	27	28	29	30	31	32	33	34	35
.8	.8	.8	.8	.8	.8	.8	.8	.8	.8	.8	.8	.8	.8	.8
.7	.7	.7	.7	.7	.7	.7	.7	.7	.7	.7	.7	.7	.7	.7
.6	.6	.6	.6	.6	.6	.6	.6	.6	.6	.6	.6	.6	.6	.6
.5	.5	.5	.5	.5	.5	.5	.5	.5	.5	.5	.5	.5	.5	.5
.4	.4	.4	.4	.4	.4	.4	.4	.4	.4	.4	.4	.4	.4	.4
.3	.3	.3	.3	.3	.3	.3	.3	.3	.3	.3	.3	.3	.3	.3
.2	.2	.2	.2	.2	.2	.2	.2	.2	.2	.2	.2	.2	.2	.2
.1	.1	.1	.1	.1	.1	.1	.1	.1	.1	.1	.1	.1	.1	.1
.0	.0	.0	.0	.0	.0	.0	.0	.0	.0	.0	.0	.0	.0	.0
.9	.9	.9	.9	.9	.9	.9	.9	.9	.9	.9	.9	.9	.9	.9
.8	.8	.8	.8	.8	.8	.8	.8	.8	.8	.8	.8	.8	.8	.8
.7	.7	.7	.7	.7	.7	.7	.7	.7	.7	.7	.7	.7	.7	.7
.6	.6	.6	.6	.6	.6	.6	.6	.6	.6	.6	.6	.6	.6	.6
.5	.5	.5	.5	.5	.5	.5	.5	.5	.5	.5	.5	.5	.5	.5
.4	.4	.4	.4	.4	.4	.4	.4	.4	.4	.4	.4	.4	.4	.4
.3	.3	.3	.3	.3	.3	.3	.3	.3	.3	.3	.3	.3	.3	.3
.2	.2	.2	.2	.2	.2	.2	.2	.2	.2	.2	.2	.2	.2	.2
.1	.1	.1	.1	.1	.1	.1	.1	.1	.1	.1	.1	.1	.1	.1
.0	.0	.0	.0	.0	.0	.0	.0	.0	.0	.0	.0	.0	.0	.0

Daily Notes

1 ________
2 ________
3 ________
4 ________
5 ________
6 ________
7 ________
8 ________
9 ________
10 ________
11 ________
12 ________
13 ________
14 ________
15 ________
16 ________
17 ________
18 ________
19 ________
20 ________
21 ________
22 ________
23 ________
24 ________
25 ________
26 ________
27 ________
28 ________
29 ________
30 ________
31 ________
32 ________
33 ________
34 ________
35 ________

Cycle: ____ Month(s): ____________ Year: ______ Length: _________

Cycle Day	1	2	3	4	5	6	7	8	9	10	11	12	13	14	15	16	17	18	19	20
Weekday																				
Date																				
Mucus Pattern																				
Sensation																				
Mucus Description																				
Sex																				
Cervical Position																				

Cycle Day	1	2	3	4	5	6	7	8	9	10	11	12	13	14	15	16	17	18	19	20
Time																				
Luteal Phase Count																				
Temperature	.8	.8	.8	.8	.8	.8	.8	.8	.8	.8	.8	.8	.8	.8	.8	.8	.8	.8	.8	.8
	.7	.7	.7	.7	.7	.7	.7	.7	.7	.7	.7	.7	.7	.7	.7	.7	.7	.7	.7	.7
	.6	.6	.6	.6	.6	.6	.6	.6	.6	.6	.6	.6	.6	.6	.6	.6	.6	.6	.6	.6
	.5	.5	.5	.5	.5	.5	.5	.5	.5	.5	.5	.5	.5	.5	.5	.5	.5	.5	.5	.5
98°	.4	.4	.4	.4	.4	.4	.4	.4	.4	.4	.4	.4	.4	.4	.4	.4	.4	.4	.4	.4
	.3	.3	.3	.3	.3	.3	.3	.3	.3	.3	.3	.3	.3	.3	.3	.3	.3	.3	.3	.3
	.2	.2	.2	.2	.2	.2	.2	.2	.2	.2	.2	.2	.2	.2	.2	.2	.2	.2	.2	.2
	.1	.1	.1	.1	.1	.1	.1	.1	.1	.1	.1	.1	.1	.1	.1	.1	.1	.1	.1	.1
	.0	.0	.0	.0	.0	.0	.0	.0	.0	.0	.0	.0	.0	.0	.0	.0	.0	.0	.0	.0
	.9	.9	.9	.9	.9	.9	.9	.9	.9	.9	.9	.9	.9	.9	.9	.9	.9	.9	.9	.9
	.8	.8	.8	.8	.8	.8	.8	.8	.8	.8	.8	.8	.8	.8	.8	.8	.8	.8	.8	.8
	.7	.7	.7	.7	.7	.7	.7	.7	.7	.7	.7	.7	.7	.7	.7	.7	.7	.7	.7	.7
	.6	.6	.6	.6	.6	.6	.6	.6	.6	.6	.6	.6	.6	.6	.6	.6	.6	.6	.6	.6
97°	.5	.5	.5	.5	.5	.5	.5	.5	.5	.5	.5	.5	.5	.5	.5	.5	.5	.5	.5	.5
	.4	.4	.4	.4	.4	.4	.4	.4	.4	.4	.4	.4	.4	.4	.4	.4	.4	.4	.4	.4
	.3	.3	.3	.3	.3	.3	.3	.3	.3	.3	.3	.3	.3	.3	.3	.3	.3	.3	.3	.3
	.2	.2	.2	.2	.2	.2	.2	.2	.2	.2	.2	.2	.2	.2	.2	.2	.2	.2	.2	.2
	.1	.1	.1	.1	.1	.1	.1	.1	.1	.1	.1	.1	.1	.1	.1	.1	.1	.1	.1	.1
	.0	.0	.0	.0	.0	.0	.0	.0	.0	.0	.0	.0	.0	.0	.0	.0	.0	.0	.0	.0

Luteal Phase: ________ **Ovulation:** ________

21	22	23	24	25	26	27	28	29	30	31	32	33	34	35
21	22	23	24	25	26	27	28	29	30	31	32	33	34	35
.8	.8	.8	.8	.8	.8	.8	.8	.8	.8	.8	.8	.8	.8	.8
.7	.7	.7	.7	.7	.7	.7	.7	.7	.7	.7	.7	.7	.7	.7
.6	.6	.6	.6	.6	.6	.6	.6	.6	.6	.6	.6	.6	.6	.6
.5	.5	.5	.5	.5	.5	.5	.5	.5	.5	.5	.5	.5	.5	.5
.4	.4	.4	.4	.4	.4	.4	.4	.4	.4	.4	.4	.4	.4	.4
.3	.3	.3	.3	.3	.3	.3	.3	.3	.3	.3	.3	.3	.3	.3
.2	.2	.2	.2	.2	.2	.2	.2	.2	.2	.2	.2	.2	.2	.2
.1	.1	.1	.1	.1	.1	.1	.1	.1	.1	.1	.1	.1	.1	.1
.0	.0	.0	.0	.0	.0	.0	.0	.0	.0	.0	.0	.0	.0	.0
.9	.9	.9	.9	.9	.9	.9	.9	.9	.9	.9	.9	.9	.9	.9
.8	.8	.8	.8	.8	.8	.8	.8	.8	.8	.8	.8	.8	.8	.8
.7	.7	.7	.7	.7	.7	.7	.7	.7	.7	.7	.7	.7	.7	.7
.6	.6	.6	.6	.6	.6	.6	.6	.6	.6	.6	.6	.6	.6	.6
.5	.5	.5	.5	.5	.5	.5	.5	.5	.5	.5	.5	.5	.5	.5
.4	.4	.4	.4	.4	.4	.4	.4	.4	.4	.4	.4	.4	.4	.4
.3	.3	.3	.3	.3	.3	.3	.3	.3	.3	.3	.3	.3	.3	.3
.2	.2	.2	.2	.2	.2	.2	.2	.2	.2	.2	.2	.2	.2	.2
.1	.1	.1	.1	.1	.1	.1	.1	.1	.1	.1	.1	.1	.1	.1
.0	.0	.0	.0	.0	.0	.0	.0	.0	.0	.0	.0	.0	.0	.0

Daily Notes

1 ______________________
2 ______________________
3 ______________________
4 ______________________
5 ______________________
6 ______________________
7 ______________________
8 ______________________
9 ______________________
10 ______________________
11 ______________________
12 ______________________
13 ______________________
14 ______________________
15 ______________________
16 ______________________
17 ______________________
18 ______________________
19 ______________________
20 ______________________
21 ______________________
22 ______________________
23 ______________________
24 ______________________
25 ______________________
26 ______________________
27 ______________________
28 ______________________
29 ______________________
30 ______________________
31 ______________________
32 ______________________
33 ______________________
34 ______________________
35 ______________________

Cycle: ____ Month(s): ____________ Year: ______ Length: _________

Cycle Day	1	2	3	4	5	6	7	8	9	10	11	12	13	14	15	16	17	18	19	20
Weekday																				
Date																				
Mucus Pattern																				
Sensation																				
Mucus Description																				
Sex																				
Cervical Position																				

Cycle Day	1	2	3	4	5	6	7	8	9	10	11	12	13	14	15	16	17	18	19	20
Time																				
Luteal Phase Count																				
Temperature	.8	.8	.8	.8	.8	.8	.8	.8	.8	.8	.8	.8	.8	.8	.8	.8	.8	.8	.8	.8
	.7	.7	.7	.7	.7	.7	.7	.7	.7	.7	.7	.7	.7	.7	.7	.7	.7	.7	.7	.7
	.6	.6	.6	.6	.6	.6	.6	.6	.6	.6	.6	.6	.6	.6	.6	.6	.6	.6	.6	.6
	.5	.5	.5	.5	.5	.5	.5	.5	.5	.5	.5	.5	.5	.5	.5	.5	.5	.5	.5	.5
98°	.4	.4	.4	.4	.4	.4	.4	.4	.4	.4	.4	.4	.4	.4	.4	.4	.4	.4	.4	.4
	.3	.3	.3	.3	.3	.3	.3	.3	.3	.3	.3	.3	.3	.3	.3	.3	.3	.3	.3	.3
	.2	.2	.2	.2	.2	.2	.2	.2	.2	.2	.2	.2	.2	.2	.2	.2	.2	.2	.2	.2
	.1	.1	.1	.1	.1	.1	.1	.1	.1	.1	.1	.1	.1	.1	.1	.1	.1	.1	.1	.1
	.0	.0	.0	.0	.0	.0	.0	.0	.0	.0	.0	.0	.0	.0	.0	.0	.0	.0	.0	.0
	.9	.9	.9	.9	.9	.9	.9	.9	.9	.9	.9	.9	.9	.9	.9	.9	.9	.9	.9	.9
	.8	.8	.8	.8	.8	.8	.8	.8	.8	.8	.8	.8	.8	.8	.8	.8	.8	.8	.8	.8
	.7	.7	.7	.7	.7	.7	.7	.7	.7	.7	.7	.7	.7	.7	.7	.7	.7	.7	.7	.7
	.6	.6	.6	.6	.6	.6	.6	.6	.6	.6	.6	.6	.6	.6	.6	.6	.6	.6	.6	.6
97°	.5	.5	.5	.5	.5	.5	.5	.5	.5	.5	.5	.5	.5	.5	.5	.5	.5	.5	.5	.5
	.4	.4	.4	.4	.4	.4	.4	.4	.4	.4	.4	.4	.4	.4	.4	.4	.4	.4	.4	.4
	.3	.3	.3	.3	.3	.3	.3	.3	.3	.3	.3	.3	.3	.3	.3	.3	.3	.3	.3	.3
	.2	.2	.2	.2	.2	.2	.2	.2	.2	.2	.2	.2	.2	.2	.2	.2	.2	.2	.2	.2
	.1	.1	.1	.1	.1	.1	.1	.1	.1	.1	.1	.1	.1	.1	.1	.1	.1	.1	.1	.1
	.0	.0	.0	.0	.0	.0	.0	.0	.0	.0	.0	.0	.0	.0	.0	.0	.0	.0	.0	.0

Luteal Phase: ________ **Ovulation:** __________

21	22	23	24	25	26	27	28	29	30	31	32	33	34	35

21	22	23	24	25	26	27	28	29	30	31	32	33	34	35
.8	.8	.8	.8	.8	.8	.8	.8	.8	.8	.8	.8	.8	.8	.8
.7	.7	.7	.7	.7	.7	.7	.7	.7	.7	.7	.7	.7	.7	.7
.6	.6	.6	.6	.6	.6	.6	.6	.6	.6	.6	.6	.6	.6	.6
.5	.5	.5	.5	.5	.5	.5	.5	.5	.5	.5	.5	.5	.5	.5
.4	.4	.4	.4	.4	.4	.4	.4	.4	.4	.4	.4	.4	.4	.4
.3	.3	.3	.3	.3	.3	.3	.3	.3	.3	.3	.3	.3	.3	.3
.2	.2	.2	.2	.2	.2	.2	.2	.2	.2	.2	.2	.2	.2	.2
.1	.1	.1	.1	.1	.1	.1	.1	.1	.1	.1	.1	.1	.1	.1
.0	.0	.0	.0	.0	.0	.0	.0	.0	.0	.0	.0	.0	.0	.0
.9	.9	.9	.9	.9	.9	.9	.9	.9	.9	.9	.9	.9	.9	.9
.8	.8	.8	.8	.8	.8	.8	.8	.8	.8	.8	.8	.8	.8	.8
.7	.7	.7	.7	.7	.7	.7	.7	.7	.7	.7	.7	.7	.7	.7
.6	.6	.6	.6	.6	.6	.6	.6	.6	.6	.6	.6	.6	.6	.6
.5	.5	.5	.5	.5	.5	.5	.5	.5	.5	.5	.5	.5	.5	.5
.4	.4	.4	.4	.4	.4	.4	.4	.4	.4	.4	.4	.4	.4	.4
.3	.3	.3	.3	.3	.3	.3	.3	.3	.3	.3	.3	.3	.3	.3
.2	.2	.2	.2	.2	.2	.2	.2	.2	.2	.2	.2	.2	.2	.2
.1	.1	.1	.1	.1	.1	.1	.1	.1	.1	.1	.1	.1	.1	.1
.0	.0	.0	.0	.0	.0	.0	.0	.0	.0	.0	.0	.0	.0	.0

Daily Notes

1 ______
2 ______
3 ______
4 ______
5 ______
6 ______
7 ______
8 ______
9 ______
10 ______
11 ______
12 ______
13 ______
14 ______
15 ______
16 ______
17 ______
18 ______
19 ______
20 ______
21 ______
22 ______
23 ______
24 ______
25 ______
26 ______
27 ______
28 ______
29 ______
30 ______
31 ______
32 ______
33 ______
34 ______
35 ______

Cycle: ____ **Month(s):** ____________ **Year:** ______ **Length:** ________

Cycle Day	1	2	3	4	5	6	7	8	9	10	11	12	13	14	15	16	17	18	19	20
Weekday																				
Date																				
Mucus Pattern																				
Sensation																				
Mucus Description																				
Sex	○	○	○	○	○	○	○	○	○	○	○	○	○	○	○	○	○	○	○	○
Cervical Position																				
	○	○	○	○	○	○	○	○	○	○	○	○	○	○	○	○	○	○	○	○

Cycle Day	1	2	3	4	5	6	7	8	9	10	11	12	13	14	15	16	17	18	19	20
Time																				
Luteal Phase Count																				
Temperature	.8	.8	.8	.8	.8	.8	.8	.8	.8	.8	.8	.8	.8	.8	.8	.8	.8	.8	.8	.8
	.7	.7	.7	.7	.7	.7	.7	.7	.7	.7	.7	.7	.7	.7	.7	.7	.7	.7	.7	.7
	.6	.6	.6	.6	.6	.6	.6	.6	.6	.6	.6	.6	.6	.6	.6	.6	.6	.6	.6	.6
	.5	.5	.5	.5	.5	.5	.5	.5	.5	.5	.5	.5	.5	.5	.5	.5	.5	.5	.5	.5
98°	.4	.4	.4	.4	.4	.4	.4	.4	.4	.4	.4	.4	.4	.4	.4	.4	.4	.4	.4	.4
	.3	.3	.3	.3	.3	.3	.3	.3	.3	.3	.3	.3	.3	.3	.3	.3	.3	.3	.3	.3
	.2	.2	.2	.2	.2	.2	.2	.2	.2	.2	.2	.2	.2	.2	.2	.2	.2	.2	.2	.2
	.1	.1	.1	.1	.1	.1	.1	.1	.1	.1	.1	.1	.1	.1	.1	.1	.1	.1	.1	.1
	.0	.0	.0	.0	.0	.0	.0	.0	.0	.0	.0	.0	.0	.0	.0	.0	.0	.0	.0	.0
	.9	.9	.9	.9	.9	.9	.9	.9	.9	.9	.9	.9	.9	.9	.9	.9	.9	.9	.9	.9
	.8	.8	.8	.8	.8	.8	.8	.8	.8	.8	.8	.8	.8	.8	.8	.8	.8	.8	.8	.8
	.7	.7	.7	.7	.7	.7	.7	.7	.7	.7	.7	.7	.7	.7	.7	.7	.7	.7	.7	.7
	.6	.6	.6	.6	.6	.6	.6	.6	.6	.6	.6	.6	.6	.6	.6	.6	.6	.6	.6	.6
97°	.5	.5	.5	.5	.5	.5	.5	.5	.5	.5	.5	.5	.5	.5	.5	.5	.5	.5	.5	.5
	.4	.4	.4	.4	.4	.4	.4	.4	.4	.4	.4	.4	.4	.4	.4	.4	.4	.4	.4	.4
	.3	.3	.3	.3	.3	.3	.3	.3	.3	.3	.3	.3	.3	.3	.3	.3	.3	.3	.3	.3
	.2	.2	.2	.2	.2	.2	.2	.2	.2	.2	.2	.2	.2	.2	.2	.2	.2	.2	.2	.2
	.1	.1	.1	.1	.1	.1	.1	.1	.1	.1	.1	.1	.1	.1	.1	.1	.1	.1	.1	.1
	.0	.0	.0	.0	.0	.0	.0	.0	.0	.0	.0	.0	.0	.0	.0	.0	.0	.0	.0	.0

Luteal Phase: ________ **Ovulation:** __________

21 22 23 24 25 26 27 28 29 30 31 32 33 34 35

21	22	23	24	25	26	27	28	29	30	31	32	33	34	35
.8	.8	.8	.8	.8	.8	.8	.8	.8	.8	.8	.8	.8	.8	.8
.7	.7	.7	.7	.7	.7	.7	.7	.7	.7	.7	.7	.7	.7	.7
.6	.6	.6	.6	.6	.6	.6	.6	.6	.6	.6	.6	.6	.6	.6
.5	.5	.5	.5	.5	.5	.5	.5	.5	.5	.5	.5	.5	.5	.5
.4	.4	.4	.4	.4	.4	.4	.4	.4	.4	.4	.4	.4	.4	.4
.3	.3	.3	.3	.3	.3	.3	.3	.3	.3	.3	.3	.3	.3	.3
.2	.2	.2	.2	.2	.2	.2	.2	.2	.2	.2	.2	.2	.2	.2
.1	.1	.1	.1	.1	.1	.1	.1	.1	.1	.1	.1	.1	.1	.1
.0	.0	.0	.0	.0	.0	.0	.0	.0	.0	.0	.0	.0	.0	.0
.9	.9	.9	.9	.9	.9	.9	.9	.9	.9	.9	.9	.9	.9	.9
.8	.8	.8	.8	.8	.8	.8	.8	.8	.8	.8	.8	.8	.8	.8
.7	.7	.7	.7	.7	.7	.7	.7	.7	.7	.7	.7	.7	.7	.7
.6	.6	.6	.6	.6	.6	.6	.6	.6	.6	.6	.6	.6	.6	.6
.5	.5	.5	.5	.5	.5	.5	.5	.5	.5	.5	.5	.5	.5	.5
.4	.4	.4	.4	.4	.4	.4	.4	.4	.4	.4	.4	.4	.4	.4
.3	.3	.3	.3	.3	.3	.3	.3	.3	.3	.3	.3	.3	.3	.3
.2	.2	.2	.2	.2	.2	.2	.2	.2	.2	.2	.2	.2	.2	.2
.1	.1	.1	.1	.1	.1	.1	.1	.1	.1	.1	.1	.1	.1	.1
.0	.0	.0	.0	.0	.0	.0	.0	.0	.0	.0	.0	.0	.0	.0

Daily Notes

1 ______
2 ______
3 ______
4 ______
5 ______
6 ______
7 ______
8 ______
9 ______
10 ______
11 ______
12 ______
13 ______
14 ______
15 ______
16 ______
17 ______
18 ______
19 ______
20 ______
21 ______
22 ______
23 ______
24 ______
25 ______
26 ______
27 ______
28 ______
29 ______
30 ______
31 ______
32 ______
33 ______
34 ______
35 ______

Cycle: ____ Month(s): ____________ Year: ______ Length: ________

Cycle Day	1	2	3	4	5	6	7	8	9	10	11	12	13	14	15	16	17	18	19	20
Weekday																				
Date																				
Mucus Pattern																				
Sensation																				
Mucus Description																				
Sex	○	○	○	○	○	○	○	○	○	○	○	○	○	○	○	○	○	○	○	○
Cervical Position																				
	○	○	○	○	○	○	○	○	○	○	○	○	○	○	○	○	○	○	○	○

Cycle Day	1	2	3	4	5	6	7	8	9	10	11	12	13	14	15	16	17	18	19	20
Time																				
Luteal Phase Count																				
Temperature	.8	.8	.8	.8	.8	.8	.8	.8	.8	.8	.8	.8	.8	.8	.8	.8	.8	.8	.8	.8
	.7	.7	.7	.7	.7	.7	.7	.7	.7	.7	.7	.7	.7	.7	.7	.7	.7	.7	.7	.7
	.6	.6	.6	.6	.6	.6	.6	.6	.6	.6	.6	.6	.6	.6	.6	.6	.6	.6	.6	.6
	.5	.5	.5	.5	.5	.5	.5	.5	.5	.5	.5	.5	.5	.5	.5	.5	.5	.5	.5	.5
98°	.4	.4	.4	.4	.4	.4	.4	.4	.4	.4	.4	.4	.4	.4	.4	.4	.4	.4	.4	.4
	.3	.3	.3	.3	.3	.3	.3	.3	.3	.3	.3	.3	.3	.3	.3	.3	.3	.3	.3	.3
	.2	.2	.2	.2	.2	.2	.2	.2	.2	.2	.2	.2	.2	.2	.2	.2	.2	.2	.2	.2
	.1	.1	.1	.1	.1	.1	.1	.1	.1	.1	.1	.1	.1	.1	.1	.1	.1	.1	.1	.1
	.0	.0	.0	.0	.0	.0	.0	.0	.0	.0	.0	.0	.0	.0	.0	.0	.0	.0	.0	.0
	.9	.9	.9	.9	.9	.9	.9	.9	.9	.9	.9	.9	.9	.9	.9	.9	.9	.9	.9	.9
	.8	.8	.8	.8	.8	.8	.8	.8	.8	.8	.8	.8	.8	.8	.8	.8	.8	.8	.8	.8
	.7	.7	.7	.7	.7	.7	.7	.7	.7	.7	.7	.7	.7	.7	.7	.7	.7	.7	.7	.7
	.6	.6	.6	.6	.6	.6	.6	.6	.6	.6	.6	.6	.6	.6	.6	.6	.6	.6	.6	.6
97°	.5	.5	.5	.5	.5	.5	.5	.5	.5	.5	.5	.5	.5	.5	.5	.5	.5	.5	.5	.5
	.4	.4	.4	.4	.4	.4	.4	.4	.4	.4	.4	.4	.4	.4	.4	.4	.4	.4	.4	.4
	.3	.3	.3	.3	.3	.3	.3	.3	.3	.3	.3	.3	.3	.3	.3	.3	.3	.3	.3	.3
	.2	.2	.2	.2	.2	.2	.2	.2	.2	.2	.2	.2	.2	.2	.2	.2	.2	.2	.2	.2
	.1	.1	.1	.1	.1	.1	.1	.1	.1	.1	.1	.1	.1	.1	.1	.1	.1	.1	.1	.1
	.0	.0	.0	.0	.0	.0	.0	.0	.0	.0	.0	.0	.0	.0	.0	.0	.0	.0	.0	.0

Luteal Phase: ________ **Ovulation:** __________

21	22	23	24	25	26	27	28	29	30	31	32	33	34	35
21	22	23	24	25	26	27	28	29	30	31	32	33	34	35
.8	.8	.8	.8	.8	.8	.8	.8	.8	.8	.8	.8	.8	.8	.8
.7	.7	.7	.7	.7	.7	.7	.7	.7	.7	.7	.7	.7	.7	.7
.6	.6	.6	.6	.6	.6	.6	.6	.6	.6	.6	.6	.6	.6	.6
.5	.5	.5	.5	.5	.5	.5	.5	.5	.5	.5	.5	.5	.5	.5
.4	.4	.4	.4	.4	.4	.4	.4	.4	.4	.4	.4	.4	.4	.4
.3	.3	.3	.3	.3	.3	.3	.3	.3	.3	.3	.3	.3	.3	.3
.2	.2	.2	.2	.2	.2	.2	.2	.2	.2	.2	.2	.2	.2	.2
.1	.1	.1	.1	.1	.1	.1	.1	.1	.1	.1	.1	.1	.1	.1
.0	.0	.0	.0	.0	.0	.0	.0	.0	.0	.0	.0	.0	.0	.0
.9	.9	.9	.9	.9	.9	.9	.9	.9	.9	.9	.9	.9	.9	.9
.8	.8	.8	.8	.8	.8	.8	.8	.8	.8	.8	.8	.8	.8	.8
.7	.7	.7	.7	.7	.7	.7	.7	.7	.7	.7	.7	.7	.7	.7
.6	.6	.6	.6	.6	.6	.6	.6	.6	.6	.6	.6	.6	.6	.6
.5	.5	.5	.5	.5	.5	.5	.5	.5	.5	.5	.5	.5	.5	.5
.4	.4	.4	.4	.4	.4	.4	.4	.4	.4	.4	.4	.4	.4	.4
.3	.3	.3	.3	.3	.3	.3	.3	.3	.3	.3	.3	.3	.3	.3
.2	.2	.2	.2	.2	.2	.2	.2	.2	.2	.2	.2	.2	.2	.2
.1	.1	.1	.1	.1	.1	.1	.1	.1	.1	.1	.1	.1	.1	.1
.0	.0	.0	.0	.0	.0	.0	.0	.0	.0	.0	.0	.0	.0	.0

Daily Notes

1 ______
2 ______
3 ______
4 ______
5 ______
6 ______
7 ______
8 ______
9 ______
10 ______
11 ______
12 ______
13 ______
14 ______
15 ______
16 ______
17 ______
18 ______
19 ______
20 ______
21 ______
22 ______
23 ______
24 ______
25 ______
26 ______
27 ______
28 ______
29 ______
30 ______
31 ______
32 ______
33 ______
34 ______
35 ______

Cycle: ____ Month(s): ____________ Year: ______ Length: _________

Cycle Day	1	2	3	4	5	6	7	8	9	10	11	12	13	14	15	16	17	18	19	20
Weekday																				
Date																				
Mucus Pattern																				
Sensation																				
Mucus Description																				
Sex																				
Cervical Position																				

Cycle Day	1	2	3	4	5	6	7	8	9	10	11	12	13	14	15	16	17	18	19	20
Time																				
Luteal Phase Count																				
Temperature	.8	.8	.8	.8	.8	.8	.8	.8	.8	.8	.8	.8	.8	.8	.8	.8	.8	.8	.8	.8
	.7	.7	.7	.7	.7	.7	.7	.7	.7	.7	.7	.7	.7	.7	.7	.7	.7	.7	.7	.7
	.6	.6	.6	.6	.6	.6	.6	.6	.6	.6	.6	.6	.6	.6	.6	.6	.6	.6	.6	.6
	.5	.5	.5	.5	.5	.5	.5	.5	.5	.5	.5	.5	.5	.5	.5	.5	.5	.5	.5	.5
98°	.4	.4	.4	.4	.4	.4	.4	.4	.4	.4	.4	.4	.4	.4	.4	.4	.4	.4	.4	.4
	.3	.3	.3	.3	.3	.3	.3	.3	.3	.3	.3	.3	.3	.3	.3	.3	.3	.3	.3	.3
	.2	.2	.2	.2	.2	.2	.2	.2	.2	.2	.2	.2	.2	.2	.2	.2	.2	.2	.2	.2
	.1	.1	.1	.1	.1	.1	.1	.1	.1	.1	.1	.1	.1	.1	.1	.1	.1	.1	.1	.1
	.0	.0	.0	.0	.0	.0	.0	.0	.0	.0	.0	.0	.0	.0	.0	.0	.0	.0	.0	.0
	.9	.9	.9	.9	.9	.9	.9	.9	.9	.9	.9	.9	.9	.9	.9	.9	.9	.9	.9	.9
	.8	.8	.8	.8	.8	.8	.8	.8	.8	.8	.8	.8	.8	.8	.8	.8	.8	.8	.8	.8
	.7	.7	.7	.7	.7	.7	.7	.7	.7	.7	.7	.7	.7	.7	.7	.7	.7	.7	.7	.7
	.6	.6	.6	.6	.6	.6	.6	.6	.6	.6	.6	.6	.6	.6	.6	.6	.6	.6	.6	.6
97°	.5	.5	.5	.5	.5	.5	.5	.5	.5	.5	.5	.5	.5	.5	.5	.5	.5	.5	.5	.5
	.4	.4	.4	.4	.4	.4	.4	.4	.4	.4	.4	.4	.4	.4	.4	.4	.4	.4	.4	.4
	.3	.3	.3	.3	.3	.3	.3	.3	.3	.3	.3	.3	.3	.3	.3	.3	.3	.3	.3	.3
	.2	.2	.2	.2	.2	.2	.2	.2	.2	.2	.2	.2	.2	.2	.2	.2	.2	.2	.2	.2
	.1	.1	.1	.1	.1	.1	.1	.1	.1	.1	.1	.1	.1	.1	.1	.1	.1	.1	.1	.1
	.0	.0	.0	.0	.0	.0	.0	.0	.0	.0	.0	.0	.0	.0	.0	.0	.0	.0	.0	.0

Luteal Phase: ________ **Ovulation:** __________

21	22	23	24	25	26	27	28	29	30	31	32	33	34	35
.8	.8	.8	.8	.8	.8	.8	.8	.8	.8	.8	.8	.8	.8	.8
.7	.7	.7	.7	.7	.7	.7	.7	.7	.7	.7	.7	.7	.7	.7
.6	.6	.6	.6	.6	.6	.6	.6	.6	.6	.6	.6	.6	.6	.6
.5	.5	.5	.5	.5	.5	.5	.5	.5	.5	.5	.5	.5	.5	.5
.4	.4	.4	.4	.4	.4	.4	.4	.4	.4	.4	.4	.4	.4	.4
.3	.3	.3	.3	.3	.3	.3	.3	.3	.3	.3	.3	.3	.3	.3
.2	.2	.2	.2	.2	.2	.2	.2	.2	.2	.2	.2	.2	.2	.2
.1	.1	.1	.1	.1	.1	.1	.1	.1	.1	.1	.1	.1	.1	.1
.0	.0	.0	.0	.0	.0	.0	.0	.0	.0	.0	.0	.0	.0	.0
.9	.9	.9	.9	.9	.9	.9	.9	.9	.9	.9	.9	.9	.9	.9
.8	.8	.8	.8	.8	.8	.8	.8	.8	.8	.8	.8	.8	.8	.8
.7	.7	.7	.7	.7	.7	.7	.7	.7	.7	.7	.7	.7	.7	.7
.6	.6	.6	.6	.6	.6	.6	.6	.6	.6	.6	.6	.6	.6	.6
.5	.5	.5	.5	.5	.5	.5	.5	.5	.5	.5	.5	.5	.5	.5
.4	.4	.4	.4	.4	.4	.4	.4	.4	.4	.4	.4	.4	.4	.4
.3	.3	.3	.3	.3	.3	.3	.3	.3	.3	.3	.3	.3	.3	.3
.2	.2	.2	.2	.2	.2	.2	.2	.2	.2	.2	.2	.2	.2	.2
.1	.1	.1	.1	.1	.1	.1	.1	.1	.1	.1	.1	.1	.1	.1
.0	.0	.0	.0	.0	.0	.0	.0	.0	.0	.0	.0	.0	.0	.0

Daily Notes

1 ____
2 ____
3 ____
4 ____
5 ____
6 ____
7 ____
8 ____
9 ____
10 ____
11 ____
12 ____
13 ____
14 ____
15 ____
16 ____
17 ____
18 ____
19 ____
20 ____
21 ____
22 ____
23 ____
24 ____
25 ____
26 ____
27 ____
28 ____
29 ____
30 ____
31 ____
32 ____
33 ____
34 ____
35 ____

Cycle: ____ Month(s): ____________ Year: ______ Length: __________

Cycle Day	1	2	3	4	5	6	7	8	9	10	11	12	13	14	15	16	17	18	19	20
Weekday																				
Date																				
Mucus Pattern																				
Sensation																				
Mucus Description																				
Sex																				
Cervical Position																				

Cycle Day	1	2	3	4	5	6	7	8	9	10	11	12	13	14	15	16	17	18	19	20
Time																				
Luteal Phase Count																				
Temperature	.8	.8	.8	.8	.8	.8	.8	.8	.8	.8	.8	.8	.8	.8	.8	.8	.8	.8	.8	.8
	.7	.7	.7	.7	.7	.7	.7	.7	.7	.7	.7	.7	.7	.7	.7	.7	.7	.7	.7	.7
	.6	.6	.6	.6	.6	.6	.6	.6	.6	.6	.6	.6	.6	.6	.6	.6	.6	.6	.6	.6
	.5	.5	.5	.5	.5	.5	.5	.5	.5	.5	.5	.5	.5	.5	.5	.5	.5	.5	.5	.5
98°	.4	.4	.4	.4	.4	.4	.4	.4	.4	.4	.4	.4	.4	.4	.4	.4	.4	.4	.4	.4
	.3	.3	.3	.3	.3	.3	.3	.3	.3	.3	.3	.3	.3	.3	.3	.3	.3	.3	.3	.3
	.2	.2	.2	.2	.2	.2	.2	.2	.2	.2	.2	.2	.2	.2	.2	.2	.2	.2	.2	.2
	.1	.1	.1	.1	.1	.1	.1	.1	.1	.1	.1	.1	.1	.1	.1	.1	.1	.1	.1	.1
	.0	.0	.0	.0	.0	.0	.0	.0	.0	.0	.0	.0	.0	.0	.0	.0	.0	.0	.0	.0
	.9	.9	.9	.9	.9	.9	.9	.9	.9	.9	.9	.9	.9	.9	.9	.9	.9	.9	.9	.9
	.8	.8	.8	.8	.8	.8	.8	.8	.8	.8	.8	.8	.8	.8	.8	.8	.8	.8	.8	.8
	.7	.7	.7	.7	.7	.7	.7	.7	.7	.7	.7	.7	.7	.7	.7	.7	.7	.7	.7	.7
	.6	.6	.6	.6	.6	.6	.6	.6	.6	.6	.6	.6	.6	.6	.6	.6	.6	.6	.6	.6
97°	.5	.5	.5	.5	.5	.5	.5	.5	.5	.5	.5	.5	.5	.5	.5	.5	.5	.5	.5	.5
	.4	.4	.4	.4	.4	.4	.4	.4	.4	.4	.4	.4	.4	.4	.4	.4	.4	.4	.4	.4
	.3	.3	.3	.3	.3	.3	.3	.3	.3	.3	.3	.3	.3	.3	.3	.3	.3	.3	.3	.3
	.2	.2	.2	.2	.2	.2	.2	.2	.2	.2	.2	.2	.2	.2	.2	.2	.2	.2	.2	.2
	.1	.1	.1	.1	.1	.1	.1	.1	.1	.1	.1	.1	.1	.1	.1	.1	.1	.1	.1	.1
	.0	.0	.0	.0	.0	.0	.0	.0	.0	.0	.0	.0	.0	.0	.0	.0	.0	.0	.0	.0

Luteal Phase: ________ **Ovulation:** __________

21	22	23	24	25	26	27	28	29	30	31	32	33	34	35

21	22	23	24	25	26	27	28	29	30	31	32	33	34	35
.8	.8	.8	.8	.8	.8	.8	.8	.8	.8	.8	.8	.8	.8	.8
.7	.7	.7	.7	.7	.7	.7	.7	.7	.7	.7	.7	.7	.7	.7
.6	.6	.6	.6	.6	.6	.6	.6	.6	.6	.6	.6	.6	.6	.6
.5	.5	.5	.5	.5	.5	.5	.5	.5	.5	.5	.5	.5	.5	.5
.4	.4	.4	.4	.4	.4	.4	.4	.4	.4	.4	.4	.4	.4	.4
.3	.3	.3	.3	.3	.3	.3	.3	.3	.3	.3	.3	.3	.3	.3
.2	.2	.2	.2	.2	.2	.2	.2	.2	.2	.2	.2	.2	.2	.2
.1	.1	.1	.1	.1	.1	.1	.1	.1	.1	.1	.1	.1	.1	.1
.0	.0	.0	.0	.0	.0	.0	.0	.0	.0	.0	.0	.0	.0	.0
.9	.9	.9	.9	.9	.9	.9	.9	.9	.9	.9	.9	.9	.9	.9
.8	.8	.8	.8	.8	.8	.8	.8	.8	.8	.8	.8	.8	.8	.8
.7	.7	.7	.7	.7	.7	.7	.7	.7	.7	.7	.7	.7	.7	.7
.6	.6	.6	.6	.6	.6	.6	.6	.6	.6	.6	.6	.6	.6	.6
.5	.5	.5	.5	.5	.5	.5	.5	.5	.5	.5	.5	.5	.5	.5
.4	.4	.4	.4	.4	.4	.4	.4	.4	.4	.4	.4	.4	.4	.4
.3	.3	.3	.3	.3	.3	.3	.3	.3	.3	.3	.3	.3	.3	.3
.2	.2	.2	.2	.2	.2	.2	.2	.2	.2	.2	.2	.2	.2	.2
.1	.1	.1	.1	.1	.1	.1	.1	.1	.1	.1	.1	.1	.1	.1
.0	.0	.0	.0	.0	.0	.0	.0	.0	.0	.0	.0	.0	.0	.0

Daily Notes

1 ____________________

2 ____________________

3 ____________________

4 ____________________

5 ____________________

6 ____________________

7 ____________________

8 ____________________

9 ____________________

10 ____________________

11 ____________________

12 ____________________

13 ____________________

14 ____________________

15 ____________________

16 ____________________

17 ____________________

18 ____________________

19 ____________________

20 ____________________

21 ____________________

22 ____________________

23 ____________________

24 ____________________

25 ____________________

26 ____________________

27 ____________________

28 ____________________

29 ____________________

30 ____________________

31 ____________________

32 ____________________

33 ____________________

34 ____________________

35 ____________________

Cycle: ____ **Month(s):** ____________ **Year:** ______ **Length:** ________

Cycle Day	1	2	3	4	5	6	7	8	9	10	11	12	13	14	15	16	17	18	19	20
Weekday																				
Date																				
Mucus Pattern																				
Sensation																				
Mucus Description																				
Sex	○	○	○	○	○	○	○	○	○	○	○	○	○	○	○	○	○	○	○	○
Cervical Position																				
	○	○	○	○	○	○	○	○	○	○	○	○	○	○	○	○	○	○	○	○

Cycle Day	1	2	3	4	5	6	7	8	9	10	11	12	13	14	15	16	17	18	19	20
Time																				
Luteal Phase Count																				
Temperature	.8	.8	.8	.8	.8	.8	.8	.8	.8	.8	.8	.8	.8	.8	.8	.8	.8	.8	.8	.8
	.7	.7	.7	.7	.7	.7	.7	.7	.7	.7	.7	.7	.7	.7	.7	.7	.7	.7	.7	.7
	.6	.6	.6	.6	.6	.6	.6	.6	.6	.6	.6	.6	.6	.6	.6	.6	.6	.6	.6	.6
	.5	.5	.5	.5	.5	.5	.5	.5	.5	.5	.5	.5	.5	.5	.5	.5	.5	.5	.5	.5
98°	.4	.4	.4	.4	.4	.4	.4	.4	.4	.4	.4	.4	.4	.4	.4	.4	.4	.4	.4	.4
	.3	.3	.3	.3	.3	.3	.3	.3	.3	.3	.3	.3	.3	.3	.3	.3	.3	.3	.3	.3
	.2	.2	.2	.2	.2	.2	.2	.2	.2	.2	.2	.2	.2	.2	.2	.2	.2	.2	.2	.2
	.1	.1	.1	.1	.1	.1	.1	.1	.1	.1	.1	.1	.1	.1	.1	.1	.1	.1	.1	.1
	.0	.0	.0	.0	.0	.0	.0	.0	.0	.0	.0	.0	.0	.0	.0	.0	.0	.0	.0	.0
	.9	.9	.9	.9	.9	.9	.9	.9	.9	.9	.9	.9	.9	.9	.9	.9	.9	.9	.9	.9
	.8	.8	.8	.8	.8	.8	.8	.8	.8	.8	.8	.8	.8	.8	.8	.8	.8	.8	.8	.8
	.7	.7	.7	.7	.7	.7	.7	.7	.7	.7	.7	.7	.7	.7	.7	.7	.7	.7	.7	.7
	.6	.6	.6	.6	.6	.6	.6	.6	.6	.6	.6	.6	.6	.6	.6	.6	.6	.6	.6	.6
97°	.5	.5	.5	.5	.5	.5	.5	.5	.5	.5	.5	.5	.5	.5	.5	.5	.5	.5	.5	.5
	.4	.4	.4	.4	.4	.4	.4	.4	.4	.4	.4	.4	.4	.4	.4	.4	.4	.4	.4	.4
	.3	.3	.3	.3	.3	.3	.3	.3	.3	.3	.3	.3	.3	.3	.3	.3	.3	.3	.3	.3
	.2	.2	.2	.2	.2	.2	.2	.2	.2	.2	.2	.2	.2	.2	.2	.2	.2	.2	.2	.2
	.1	.1	.1	.1	.1	.1	.1	.1	.1	.1	.1	.1	.1	.1	.1	.1	.1	.1	.1	.1
	.0	.0	.0	.0	.0	.0	.0	.0	.0	.0	.0	.0	.0	.0	.0	.0	.0	.0	.0	.0

Luteal Phase: __________ **Ovulation:** ____________

21	22	23	24	25	26	27	28	29	30	31	32	33	34	35

21	22	23	24	25	26	27	28	29	30	31	32	33	34	35
.8	.8	.8	.8	.8	.8	.8	.8	.8	.8	.8	.8	.8	.8	.8
.7	.7	.7	.7	.7	.7	.7	.7	.7	.7	.7	.7	.7	.7	.7
.6	.6	.6	.6	.6	.6	.6	.6	.6	.6	.6	.6	.6	.6	.6
.5	.5	.5	.5	.5	.5	.5	.5	.5	.5	.5	.5	.5	.5	.5
.4	.4	.4	.4	.4	.4	.4	.4	.4	.4	.4	.4	.4	.4	.4
.3	.3	.3	.3	.3	.3	.3	.3	.3	.3	.3	.3	.3	.3	.3
.2	.2	.2	.2	.2	.2	.2	.2	.2	.2	.2	.2	.2	.2	.2
.1	.1	.1	.1	.1	.1	.1	.1	.1	.1	.1	.1	.1	.1	.1
.0	.0	.0	.0	.0	.0	.0	.0	.0	.0	.0	.0	.0	.0	.0
.9	.9	.9	.9	.9	.9	.9	.9	.9	.9	.9	.9	.9	.9	.9
.8	.8	.8	.8	.8	.8	.8	.8	.8	.8	.8	.8	.8	.8	.8
.7	.7	.7	.7	.7	.7	.7	.7	.7	.7	.7	.7	.7	.7	.7
.6	.6	.6	.6	.6	.6	.6	.6	.6	.6	.6	.6	.6	.6	.6
.5	.5	.5	.5	.5	.5	.5	.5	.5	.5	.5	.5	.5	.5	.5
.4	.4	.4	.4	.4	.4	.4	.4	.4	.4	.4	.4	.4	.4	.4
.3	.3	.3	.3	.3	.3	.3	.3	.3	.3	.3	.3	.3	.3	.3
.2	.2	.2	.2	.2	.2	.2	.2	.2	.2	.2	.2	.2	.2	.2
.1	.1	.1	.1	.1	.1	.1	.1	.1	.1	.1	.1	.1	.1	.1
.0	.0	.0	.0	.0	.0	.0	.0	.0	.0	.0	.0	.0	.0	.0

Daily Notes

1 ____________________
2 ____________________
3 ____________________
4 ____________________
5 ____________________
6 ____________________
7 ____________________
8 ____________________
9 ____________________
10 ____________________
11 ____________________
12 ____________________
13 ____________________
14 ____________________
15 ____________________
16 ____________________
17 ____________________
18 ____________________
19 ____________________
20 ____________________
21 ____________________
22 ____________________
23 ____________________
24 ____________________
25 ____________________
26 ____________________
27 ____________________
28 ____________________
29 ____________________
30 ____________________
31 ____________________
32 ____________________
33 ____________________
34 ____________________
35 ____________________

Cycle: ____ Month(s): ____________ Year: ______ Length: ________

Cycle Day	1	2	3	4	5	6	7	8	9	10	11	12	13	14	15	16	17	18	19	20
Weekday																				
Date																				
Mucus Pattern																				
Sensation																				
Mucus Description																				
Sex																				
Cervical Position																				

Cycle Day	1	2	3	4	5	6	7	8	9	10	11	12	13	14	15	16	17	18	19	20
Time																				
Luteal Phase Count																				
Temperature	.8	.8	.8	.8	.8	.8	.8	.8	.8	.8	.8	.8	.8	.8	.8	.8	.8	.8	.8	.8
	.7	.7	.7	.7	.7	.7	.7	.7	.7	.7	.7	.7	.7	.7	.7	.7	.7	.7	.7	.7
	.6	.6	.6	.6	.6	.6	.6	.6	.6	.6	.6	.6	.6	.6	.6	.6	.6	.6	.6	.6
	.5	.5	.5	.5	.5	.5	.5	.5	.5	.5	.5	.5	.5	.5	.5	.5	.5	.5	.5	.5
98°	.4	.4	.4	.4	.4	.4	.4	.4	.4	.4	.4	.4	.4	.4	.4	.4	.4	.4	.4	.4
	.3	.3	.3	.3	.3	.3	.3	.3	.3	.3	.3	.3	.3	.3	.3	.3	.3	.3	.3	.3
	.2	.2	.2	.2	.2	.2	.2	.2	.2	.2	.2	.2	.2	.2	.2	.2	.2	.2	.2	.2
	.1	.1	.1	.1	.1	.1	.1	.1	.1	.1	.1	.1	.1	.1	.1	.1	.1	.1	.1	.1
	.0	.0	.0	.0	.0	.0	.0	.0	.0	.0	.0	.0	.0	.0	.0	.0	.0	.0	.0	.0
	.9	.9	.9	.9	.9	.9	.9	.9	.9	.9	.9	.9	.9	.9	.9	.9	.9	.9	.9	.9
	.8	.8	.8	.8	.8	.8	.8	.8	.8	.8	.8	.8	.8	.8	.8	.8	.8	.8	.8	.8
	.7	.7	.7	.7	.7	.7	.7	.7	.7	.7	.7	.7	.7	.7	.7	.7	.7	.7	.7	.7
	.6	.6	.6	.6	.6	.6	.6	.6	.6	.6	.6	.6	.6	.6	.6	.6	.6	.6	.6	.6
97°	.5	.5	.5	.5	.5	.5	.5	.5	.5	.5	.5	.5	.5	.5	.5	.5	.5	.5	.5	.5
	.4	.4	.4	.4	.4	.4	.4	.4	.4	.4	.4	.4	.4	.4	.4	.4	.4	.4	.4	.4
	.3	.3	.3	.3	.3	.3	.3	.3	.3	.3	.3	.3	.3	.3	.3	.3	.3	.3	.3	.3
	.2	.2	.2	.2	.2	.2	.2	.2	.2	.2	.2	.2	.2	.2	.2	.2	.2	.2	.2	.2
	.1	.1	.1	.1	.1	.1	.1	.1	.1	.1	.1	.1	.1	.1	.1	.1	.1	.1	.1	.1
	.0	.0	.0	.0	.0	.0	.0	.0	.0	.0	.0	.0	.0	.0	.0	.0	.0	.0	.0	.0

Luteal Phase: ________ **Ovulation:** __________

21	22	23	24	25	26	27	28	29	30	31	32	33	34	35

21	22	23	24	25	26	27	28	29	30	31	32	33	34	35
.8	.8	.8	.8	.8	.8	.8	.8	.8	.8	.8	.8	.8	.8	.8
.7	.7	.7	.7	.7	.7	.7	.7	.7	.7	.7	.7	.7	.7	.7
.6	.6	.6	.6	.6	.6	.6	.6	.6	.6	.6	.6	.6	.6	.6
.5	.5	.5	.5	.5	.5	.5	.5	.5	.5	.5	.5	.5	.5	.5
.4	.4	.4	.4	.4	.4	.4	.4	.4	.4	.4	.4	.4	.4	.4
.3	.3	.3	.3	.3	.3	.3	.3	.3	.3	.3	.3	.3	.3	.3
.2	.2	.2	.2	.2	.2	.2	.2	.2	.2	.2	.2	.2	.2	.2
.1	.1	.1	.1	.1	.1	.1	.1	.1	.1	.1	.1	.1	.1	.1
.0	.0	.0	.0	.0	.0	.0	.0	.0	.0	.0	.0	.0	.0	.0
.9	.9	.9	.9	.9	.9	.9	.9	.9	.9	.9	.9	.9	.9	.9
.8	.8	.8	.8	.8	.8	.8	.8	.8	.8	.8	.8	.8	.8	.8
.7	.7	.7	.7	.7	.7	.7	.7	.7	.7	.7	.7	.7	.7	.7
.6	.6	.6	.6	.6	.6	.6	.6	.6	.6	.6	.6	.6	.6	.6
.5	.5	.5	.5	.5	.5	.5	.5	.5	.5	.5	.5	.5	.5	.5
.4	.4	.4	.4	.4	.4	.4	.4	.4	.4	.4	.4	.4	.4	.4
.3	.3	.3	.3	.3	.3	.3	.3	.3	.3	.3	.3	.3	.3	.3
.2	.2	.2	.2	.2	.2	.2	.2	.2	.2	.2	.2	.2	.2	.2
.1	.1	.1	.1	.1	.1	.1	.1	.1	.1	.1	.1	.1	.1	.1
.0	.0	.0	.0	.0	.0	.0	.0	.0	.0	.0	.0	.0	.0	.0

Daily Notes

1 ____________________
2 ____________________
3 ____________________
4 ____________________
5 ____________________
6 ____________________
7 ____________________
8 ____________________
9 ____________________
10 ____________________
11 ____________________
12 ____________________
13 ____________________
14 ____________________
15 ____________________
16 ____________________
17 ____________________
18 ____________________
19 ____________________
20 ____________________
21 ____________________
22 ____________________
23 ____________________
24 ____________________
25 ____________________
26 ____________________
27 ____________________
28 ____________________
29 ____________________
30 ____________________
31 ____________________
32 ____________________
33 ____________________
34 ____________________
35 ____________________

Cycle: ___ Month(s): ___________ Year: _____ Length: ________

Cycle Day	1	2	3	4	5	6	7	8	9	10	11	12	13	14	15	16	17	18	19	20
Weekday																				
Date																				
Mucus Pattern																				
Sensation																				
Mucus Description																				
Sex	○	○	○	○	○	○	○	○	○	○	○	○	○	○	○	○	○	○	○	○
Cervical Position																				
	○	○	○	○	○	○	○	○	○	○	○	○	○	○	○	○	○	○	○	○

Cycle Day	1	2	3	4	5	6	7	8	9	10	11	12	13	14	15	16	17	18	19	20
Time																				
Luteal Phase Count																				
Temperature	.8	.8	.8	.8	.8	.8	.8	.8	.8	.8	.8	.8	.8	.8	.8	.8	.8	.8	.8	.8
	.7	.7	.7	.7	.7	.7	.7	.7	.7	.7	.7	.7	.7	.7	.7	.7	.7	.7	.7	.7
	.6	.6	.6	.6	.6	.6	.6	.6	.6	.6	.6	.6	.6	.6	.6	.6	.6	.6	.6	.6
	.5	.5	.5	.5	.5	.5	.5	.5	.5	.5	.5	.5	.5	.5	.5	.5	.5	.5	.5	.5
98°	.4	.4	.4	.4	.4	.4	.4	.4	.4	.4	.4	.4	.4	.4	.4	.4	.4	.4	.4	.4
	.3	.3	.3	.3	.3	.3	.3	.3	.3	.3	.3	.3	.3	.3	.3	.3	.3	.3	.3	.3
	.2	.2	.2	.2	.2	.2	.2	.2	.2	.2	.2	.2	.2	.2	.2	.2	.2	.2	.2	.2
	.1	.1	.1	.1	.1	.1	.1	.1	.1	.1	.1	.1	.1	.1	.1	.1	.1	.1	.1	.1
	.0	.0	.0	.0	.0	.0	.0	.0	.0	.0	.0	.0	.0	.0	.0	.0	.0	.0	.0	.0
	.9	.9	.9	.9	.9	.9	.9	.9	.9	.9	.9	.9	.9	.9	.9	.9	.9	.9	.9	.9
	.8	.8	.8	.8	.8	.8	.8	.8	.8	.8	.8	.8	.8	.8	.8	.8	.8	.8	.8	.8
	.7	.7	.7	.7	.7	.7	.7	.7	.7	.7	.7	.7	.7	.7	.7	.7	.7	.7	.7	.7
	.6	.6	.6	.6	.6	.6	.6	.6	.6	.6	.6	.6	.6	.6	.6	.6	.6	.6	.6	.6
97°	.5	.5	.5	.5	.5	.5	.5	.5	.5	.5	.5	.5	.5	.5	.5	.5	.5	.5	.5	.5
	.4	.4	.4	.4	.4	.4	.4	.4	.4	.4	.4	.4	.4	.4	.4	.4	.4	.4	.4	.4
	.3	.3	.3	.3	.3	.3	.3	.3	.3	.3	.3	.3	.3	.3	.3	.3	.3	.3	.3	.3
	.2	.2	.2	.2	.2	.2	.2	.2	.2	.2	.2	.2	.2	.2	.2	.2	.2	.2	.2	.2
	.1	.1	.1	.1	.1	.1	.1	.1	.1	.1	.1	.1	.1	.1	.1	.1	.1	.1	.1	.1
	.0	.0	.0	.0	.0	.0	.0	.0	.0	.0	.0	.0	.0	.0	.0	.0	.0	.0	.0	.0

Luteal Phase: ________ **Ovulation:** __________

21	22	23	24	25	26	27	28	29	30	31	32	33	34	35

21	22	23	24	25	26	27	28	29	30	31	32	33	34	35
.8	.8	.8	.8	.8	.8	.8	.8	.8	.8	.8	.8	.8	.8	.8
.7	.7	.7	.7	.7	.7	.7	.7	.7	.7	.7	.7	.7	.7	.7
.6	.6	.6	.6	.6	.6	.6	.6	.6	.6	.6	.6	.6	.6	.6
.5	.5	.5	.5	.5	.5	.5	.5	.5	.5	.5	.5	.5	.5	.5
.4	.4	.4	.4	.4	.4	.4	.4	.4	.4	.4	.4	.4	.4	.4
.3	.3	.3	.3	.3	.3	.3	.3	.3	.3	.3	.3	.3	.3	.3
.2	.2	.2	.2	.2	.2	.2	.2	.2	.2	.2	.2	.2	.2	.2
.1	.1	.1	.1	.1	.1	.1	.1	.1	.1	.1	.1	.1	.1	.1
.0	.0	.0	.0	.0	.0	.0	.0	.0	.0	.0	.0	.0	.0	.0
.9	.9	.9	.9	.9	.9	.9	.9	.9	.9	.9	.9	.9	.9	.9
.8	.8	.8	.8	.8	.8	.8	.8	.8	.8	.8	.8	.8	.8	.8
.7	.7	.7	.7	.7	.7	.7	.7	.7	.7	.7	.7	.7	.7	.7
.6	.6	.6	.6	.6	.6	.6	.6	.6	.6	.6	.6	.6	.6	.6
.5	.5	.5	.5	.5	.5	.5	.5	.5	.5	.5	.5	.5	.5	.5
.4	.4	.4	.4	.4	.4	.4	.4	.4	.4	.4	.4	.4	.4	.4
.3	.3	.3	.3	.3	.3	.3	.3	.3	.3	.3	.3	.3	.3	.3
.2	.2	.2	.2	.2	.2	.2	.2	.2	.2	.2	.2	.2	.2	.2
.1	.1	.1	.1	.1	.1	.1	.1	.1	.1	.1	.1	.1	.1	.1
.0	.0	.0	.0	.0	.0	.0	.0	.0	.0	.0	.0	.0	.0	.0

Daily Notes

1 ______________________
2 ______________________
3 ______________________
4 ______________________
5 ______________________
6 ______________________
7 ______________________
8 ______________________
9 ______________________
10 ______________________
11 ______________________
12 ______________________
13 ______________________
14 ______________________
15 ______________________
16 ______________________
17 ______________________
18 ______________________
19 ______________________
20 ______________________
21 ______________________
22 ______________________
23 ______________________
24 ______________________
25 ______________________
26 ______________________
27 ______________________
28 ______________________
29 ______________________
30 ______________________
31 ______________________
32 ______________________
33 ______________________
34 ______________________
35 ______________________

Cycle: ___ Month(s): ___________ Year: _____ Length: ________

Cycle Day	1	2	3	4	5	6	7	8	9	10	11	12	13	14	15	16	17	18	19	20
Weekday																				
Date																				
Mucus Pattern																				
Sensation																				
Mucus Description																				
Sex																				
Cervical Position																				

Cycle Day	1	2	3	4	5	6	7	8	9	10	11	12	13	14	15	16	17	18	19	20
Time																				
Luteal Phase Count																				
Temperature	.8	.8	.8	.8	.8	.8	.8	.8	.8	.8	.8	.8	.8	.8	.8	.8	.8	.8	.8	.8
	.7	.7	.7	.7	.7	.7	.7	.7	.7	.7	.7	.7	.7	.7	.7	.7	.7	.7	.7	.7
	.6	.6	.6	.6	.6	.6	.6	.6	.6	.6	.6	.6	.6	.6	.6	.6	.6	.6	.6	6
	.5	.5	.5	.5	.5	.5	.5	.5	.5	.5	.5	.5	.5	.5	.5	.5	.5	.5	.5	.5
98°	.4	.4	.4	.4	.4	.4	.4	.4	.4	.4	.4	.4	.4	.4	.4	.4	.4	.4	.4	.4
	.3	.3	.3	.3	.3	.3	.3	.3	.3	.3	.3	.3	.3	.3	.3	.3	.3	.3	.3	.3
	.2	.2	.2	.2	.2	.2	.2	.2	.2	.2	.2	.2	.2	.2	.2	.2	.2	.2	.2	.2
	.1	.1	.1	.1	.1	.1	.1	.1	.1	.1	.1	.1	.1	.1	.1	.1	.1	.1	.1	.1
	.0	.0	.0	.0	.0	.0	.0	.0	.0	.0	.0	.0	.0	.0	.0	.0	.0	.0	.0	.0
	.9	.9	.9	.9	.9	.9	.9	.9	.9	.9	.9	.9	.9	.9	.9	.9	.9	.9	.9	.9
	.8	.8	.8	.8	.8	.8	.8	.8	.8	.8	.8	.8	.8	.8	.8	.8	.8	.8	.8	.8
	.7	.7	.7	.7	.7	.7	.7	.7	.7	.7	.7	.7	.7	.7	.7	.7	.7	.7	.7	.7
	.6	.6	.6	.6	.6	.6	.6	.6	.6	.6	.6	.6	.6	.6	.6	.6	.6	.6	.6	6
97°	.5	.5	.5	.5	.5	.5	.5	.5	.5	.5	.5	.5	.5	.5	.5	.5	.5	.5	.5	5
	.4	.4	.4	.4	.4	.4	.4	.4	.4	.4	.4	.4	.4	.4	.4	.4	.4	.4	.4	.4
	.3	.3	.3	.3	.3	.3	.3	.3	.3	.3	.3	.3	.3	.3	.3	.3	.3	.3	.3	.3
	.2	.2	.2	.2	.2	.2	.2	.2	.2	.2	.2	.2	.2	.2	.2	.2	.2	.2	.2	.2
	.1	.1	.1	.1	.1	.1	.1	.1	.1	.1	.1	.1	.1	.1	.1	.1	.1	.1	.1	.1
	.0	.0	.0	.0	.0	.0	.0	.0	.0	.0	.0	.0	.0	.0	.0	.0	.0	.0	.0	.0

Luteal Phase: ________ **Ovulation:** __________

21	22	23	24	25	26	27	28	29	30	31	32	33	34	35

21	22	23	24	25	26	27	28	29	30	31	32	33	34	35
.8	.8	.8	.8	.8	.8	.8	.8	.8	.8	.8	.8	.8	.8	.8
.7	.7	.7	.7	.7	.7	.7	.7	.7	.7	.7	.7	.7	.7	.7
.6	.6	.6	.6	.6	.6	.6	.6	.6	.6	.6	.6	.6	.6	.6
.5	.5	.5	.5	.5	.5	.5	.5	.5	.5	.5	.5	.5	.5	.5
.4	.4	.4	.4	.4	.4	.4	.4	.4	.4	.4	.4	.4	.4	.4
.3	.3	.3	.3	.3	.3	.3	.3	.3	.3	.3	.3	.3	.3	.3
.2	.2	.2	.2	.2	.2	.2	.2	.2	.2	.2	.2	.2	.2	.2
.1	.1	.1	.1	.1	.1	.1	.1	.1	.1	.1	.1	.1	.1	.1
.0	.0	.0	.0	.0	.0	.0	.0	.0	.0	.0	.0	.0	.0	.0
.9	.9	.9	.9	.9	.9	.9	.9	.9	.9	.9	.9	.9	.9	.9
.8	.8	.8	.8	.8	.8	.8	.8	.8	.8	.8	.8	.8	.8	.8
.7	.7	.7	.7	.7	.7	.7	.7	.7	.7	.7	.7	.7	.7	.7
.6	.6	.6	.6	.6	.6	.6	.6	.6	.6	.6	.6	.6	.6	.6
.5	.5	.5	.5	.5	.5	.5	.5	.5	.5	.5	.5	.5	.5	.5
.4	.4	.4	.4	.4	.4	.4	.4	.4	.4	.4	.4	.4	.4	.4
.3	.3	.3	.3	.3	.3	.3	.3	.3	.3	.3	.3	.3	.3	.3
.2	.2	.2	.2	.2	.2	.2	.2	.2	.2	.2	.2	.2	.2	.2
.1	.1	.1	.1	.1	.1	.1	.1	.1	.1	.1	.1	.1	.1	.1
.0	.0	.0	.0	.0	.0	.0	.0	.0	.0	.0	.0	.0	.0	.0

Daily Notes

1 ______
2 ______
3 ______
4 ______
5 ______
6 ______
7 ______
8 ______
9 ______
10 ______
11 ______
12 ______
13 ______
14 ______
15 ______
16 ______
17 ______
18 ______
19 ______
20 ______
21 ______
22 ______
23 ______
24 ______
25 ______
26 ______
27 ______
28 ______
29 ______
30 ______
31 ______
32 ______
33 ______
34 ______
35 ______

Cycle: ___ Month(s): ___________ Year: _____ Length: ________

Cycle Day	1	2	3	4	5	6	7	8	9	10	11	12	13	14	15	16	17	18	19	20
Weekday																				
Date																				
Mucus Pattern																				
Sensation																				
Mucus Description																				
Sex																				
Cervical Position																				

Cycle Day	1	2	3	4	5	6	7	8	9	10	11	12	13	14	15	16	17	18	19	20
Time																				
Luteal Phase Count																				
Temperature	.8	.8	.8	.8	.8	.8	.8	.8	.8	.8	.8	.8	.8	.8	.8	.8	.8	.8	.8	.8
	.7	.7	.7	.7	.7	.7	.7	.7	.7	.7	.7	.7	.7	.7	.7	.7	.7	.7	.7	.7
	.6	.6	.6	.6	.6	.6	.6	.6	.6	.6	.6	.6	.6	.6	.6	.6	.6	.6	.6	.6
	.5	.5	.5	.5	.5	.5	.5	.5	.5	.5	.5	.5	.5	.5	.5	.5	.5	.5	.5	.5
98°	.4	.4	.4	.4	.4	.4	.4	.4	.4	.4	.4	.4	.4	.4	.4	.4	.4	.4	.4	.4
	.3	.3	.3	.3	.3	.3	.3	.3	.3	.3	.3	.3	.3	.3	.3	.3	.3	.3	.3	.3
	.2	.2	.2	.2	.2	.2	.2	.2	.2	.2	.2	.2	.2	.2	.2	.2	.2	.2	.2	.2
	.1	.1	.1	.1	.1	.1	.1	.1	.1	.1	.1	.1	.1	.1	.1	.1	.1	.1	.1	.1
	.0	.0	.0	.0	.0	.0	.0	.0	.0	.0	.0	.0	.0	.0	.0	.0	.0	.0	.0	.0
	.9	.9	.9	.9	.9	.9	.9	.9	.9	.9	.9	.9	.9	.9	.9	.9	.9	.9	.9	.9
	.8	.8	.8	.8	.8	.8	.8	.8	.8	.8	.8	.8	.8	.8	.8	.8	.8	.8	.8	.8
	.7	.7	.7	.7	.7	.7	.7	.7	.7	.7	.7	.7	.7	.7	.7	.7	.7	.7	.7	.7
	.6	.6	.6	.6	.6	.6	.6	.6	.6	.6	.6	.6	.6	.6	.6	.6	.6	.6	.6	.6
97°	.5	.5	.5	.5	.5	.5	.5	.5	.5	.5	.5	.5	.5	.5	.5	.5	.5	.5	.5	.5
	.4	.4	.4	.4	.4	.4	.4	.4	.4	.4	.4	.4	.4	.4	.4	.4	.4	.4	.4	.4
	.3	.3	.3	.3	.3	.3	.3	.3	.3	.3	.3	.3	.3	.3	.3	.3	.3	.3	.3	.3
	.2	.2	.2	.2	.2	.2	.2	.2	.2	.2	.2	.2	.2	.2	.2	.2	.2	.2	.2	.2
	.1	.1	.1	.1	.1	.1	.1	.1	.1	.1	.1	.1	.1	.1	.1	.1	.1	.1	.1	.1
	.0	.0	.0	.0	.0	.0	.0	.0	.0	.0	.0	.0	.0	.0	.0	.0	.0	.0	.0	.0

Luteal Phase: ________ **Ovulation:** __________

21	22	23	24	25	26	27	28	29	30	31	32	33	34	35

21	22	23	24	25	26	27	28	29	30	31	32	33	34	35
.8	.8	.8	.8	.8	.8	.8	.8	.8	.8	.8	.8	.8	.8	.8
.7	.7	.7	.7	.7	.7	.7	.7	.7	.7	.7	.7	.7	.7	.7
.6	.6	.6	.6	.6	.6	.6	.6	.6	.6	.6	.6	.6	.6	.6
.5	.5	.5	.5	.5	.5	.5	.5	.5	.5	.5	.5	.5	.5	.5
.4	.4	.4	.4	.4	.4	.4	.4	.4	.4	.4	.4	.4	.4	.4
.3	.3	.3	.3	.3	.3	.3	.3	.3	.3	.3	.3	.3	.3	.3
.2	.2	.2	.2	.2	.2	.2	.2	.2	.2	.2	.2	.2	.2	.2
.1	.1	.1	.1	.1	.1	.1	.1	.1	.1	.1	.1	.1	.1	.1
.0	.0	.0	.0	.0	.0	.0	.0	.0	.0	.0	.0	.0	.0	.0
.9	.9	.9	.9	.9	.9	.9	.9	.9	.9	.9	.9	.9	.9	.9
.8	.8	.8	.8	.8	.8	.8	.8	.8	.8	.8	.8	.8	.8	.8
.7	.7	.7	.7	.7	.7	.7	.7	.7	.7	.7	.7	.7	.7	.7
.6	.6	.6	.6	.6	.6	.6	.6	.6	.6	.6	.6	.6	.6	.6
.5	.5	.5	.5	.5	.5	.5	.5	.5	.5	.5	.5	.5	.5	.5
.4	.4	.4	.4	.4	.4	.4	.4	.4	.4	.4	.4	.4	.4	.4
.3	.3	.3	.3	.3	.3	.3	.3	.3	.3	.3	.3	.3	.3	.3
.2	.2	.2	.2	.2	.2	.2	.2	.2	.2	.2	.2	.2	.2	.2
.1	.1	.1	.1	.1	.1	.1	.1	.1	.1	.1	.1	.1	.1	.1
.0	.0	.0	.0	.0	.0	.0	.0	.0	.0	.0	.0	.0	.0	.0

Daily Notes

1 ______________________________
2 ______________________________
3 ______________________________
4 ______________________________
5 ______________________________
6 ______________________________
7 ______________________________
8 ______________________________
9 ______________________________
10 ______________________________
11 ______________________________
12 ______________________________
13 ______________________________
14 ______________________________
15 ______________________________
16 ______________________________
17 ______________________________
18 ______________________________
19 ______________________________
20 ______________________________
21 ______________________________
22 ______________________________
23 ______________________________
24 ______________________________
25 ______________________________
26 ______________________________
27 ______________________________
28 ______________________________
29 ______________________________
30 ______________________________
31 ______________________________
32 ______________________________
33 ______________________________
34 ______________________________
35 ______________________________

Cycle: ___ Month(s): __________ Year: _____ Length: _______

Cycle Day	1	2	3	4	5	6	7	8	9	10	11	12	13	14	15	16	17	18	19	20
Weekday																				
Date																				
Mucus Pattern																				
Sensation																				
Mucus Description																				
Sex																				
Cervical Position																				

Cycle Day	1	2	3	4	5	6	7	8	9	10	11	12	13	14	15	16	17	18	19	20
Time																				
Luteal Phase Count																				
Temperature	.8	.8	.8	.8	.8	.8	.8	.8	.8	.8	.8	.8	.8	.8	.8	.8	.8	.8	.8	.8
	.7	.7	.7	.7	.7	.7	.7	.7	.7	.7	.7	.7	.7	.7	.7	.7	.7	.7	.7	.7
	.6	.6	.6	.6	.6	.6	.6	.6	.6	.6	.6	.6	.6	.6	.6	.6	.6	.6	.6	.6
	.5	.5	.5	.5	.5	.5	.5	.5	.5	.5	.5	.5	.5	.5	.5	.5	.5	.5	.5	.5
98°	.4	.4	.4	.4	.4	.4	.4	.4	.4	.4	.4	.4	.4	.4	.4	.4	.4	.4	.4	.4
	.3	.3	.3	.3	.3	.3	.3	.3	.3	.3	.3	.3	.3	.3	.3	.3	.3	.3	.3	.3
	.2	.2	.2	.2	.2	.2	.2	.2	.2	.2	.2	.2	.2	.2	.2	.2	.2	.2	.2	.2
	.1	.1	.1	.1	.1	.1	.1	.1	.1	.1	.1	.1	.1	.1	.1	.1	.1	.1	.1	.1
	.0	.0	.0	.0	.0	.0	.0	.0	.0	.0	.0	.0	.0	.0	.0	.0	.0	.0	.0	.0
	.9	.9	.9	.9	.9	.9	.9	.9	.9	.9	.9	.9	.9	.9	.9	.9	.9	.9	.9	.9
	.8	.8	.8	.8	.8	.8	.8	.8	.8	.8	.8	.8	.8	.8	.8	.8	.8	.8	.8	.8
	.7	.7	.7	.7	.7	.7	.7	.7	.7	.7	.7	.7	.7	.7	.7	.7	.7	.7	.7	.7
	.6	.6	.6	.6	.6	.6	.6	.6	.6	.6	.6	.6	.6	.6	.6	.6	.6	.6	.6	.6
97°	.5	.5	.5	.5	.5	.5	.5	.5	.5	.5	.5	.5	.5	.5	.5	.5	.5	.5	.5	.5
	.4	.4	.4	.4	.4	.4	.4	.4	.4	.4	.4	.4	.4	.4	.4	.4	.4	.4	.4	.4
	.3	.3	.3	.3	.3	.3	.3	.3	.3	.3	.3	.3	.3	.3	.3	.3	.3	.3	.3	.3
	.2	.2	.2	.2	.2	.2	.2	.2	.2	.2	.2	.2	.2	.2	.2	.2	.2	.2	.2	.2
	.1	.1	.1	.1	.1	.1	.1	.1	.1	.1	.1	.1	.1	.1	.1	.1	.1	.1	.1	.1
	.0	.0	.0	.0	.0	.0	.0	.0	.0	.0	.0	.0	.0	.0	.0	.0	.0	.0	.0	.0

Luteal Phase: ________ **Ovulation:** __________

21	22	23	24	25	26	27	28	29	30	31	32	33	34	35

21	22	23	24	25	26	27	28	29	30	31	32	33	34	35
.8	.8	.8	.8	.8	.8	.8	.8	.8	.8	.8	.8	.8	.8	.8
.7	.7	.7	.7	.7	.7	.7	.7	.7	.7	.7	.7	.7	.7	.7
.6	.6	.6	.6	.6	.6	.6	.6	.6	.6	.6	.6	.6	.6	.6
.5	.5	.5	.5	.5	.5	.5	.5	.5	.5	.5	.5	.5	.5	.5
.4	.4	.4	.4	.4	.4	.4	.4	.4	.4	.4	.4	.4	.4	.4
.3	.3	.3	.3	.3	.3	.3	.3	.3	.3	.3	.3	.3	.3	.3
.2	.2	.2	.2	.2	.2	.2	.2	.2	.2	.2	.2	.2	.2	.2
.1	.1	.1	.1	.1	.1	.1	.1	.1	.1	.1	.1	.1	.1	.1
.0	.0	.0	.0	.0	.0	.0	.0	.0	.0	.0	.0	.0	.0	.0
.9	.9	.9	.9	.9	.9	.9	.9	.9	.9	.9	.9	.9	.9	.9
.8	.8	.8	.8	.8	.8	.8	.8	.8	.8	.8	.8	.8	.8	.8
.7	.7	.7	.7	.7	.7	.7	.7	.7	.7	.7	.7	.7	.7	.7
.6	.6	.6	.6	.6	.6	.6	.6	.6	.6	.6	.6	.6	.6	.6
.5	.5	.5	.5	.5	.5	.5	.5	.5	.5	.5	.5	.5	.5	.5
.4	.4	.4	.4	.4	.4	.4	.4	.4	.4	.4	.4	.4	.4	.4
.3	.3	.3	.3	.3	.3	.3	.3	.3	.3	.3	.3	.3	.3	.3
.2	.2	.2	.2	.2	.2	.2	.2	.2	.2	.2	.2	.2	.2	.2
.1	.1	.1	.1	.1	.1	.1	.1	.1	.1	.1	.1	.1	.1	.1
.0	.0	.0	.0	.0	.0	.0	.0	.0	.0	.0	.0	.0	.0	.0

Daily Notes

1 ____________________
2 ____________________
3 ____________________
4 ____________________
5 ____________________
6 ____________________
7 ____________________
8 ____________________
9 ____________________
10 ____________________
11 ____________________
12 ____________________
13 ____________________
14 ____________________
15 ____________________
16 ____________________
17 ____________________
18 ____________________
19 ____________________
20 ____________________
21 ____________________
22 ____________________
23 ____________________
24 ____________________
25 ____________________
26 ____________________
27 ____________________
28 ____________________
29 ____________________
30 ____________________
31 ____________________
32 ____________________
33 ____________________
34 ____________________
35 ____________________

Cycle: ____ Month(s): ____________ Year: ______ Length: ________

Cycle Day	1	2	3	4	5	6	7	8	9	10	11	12	13	14	15	16	17	18	19	20
Weekday																				
Date																				
Mucus Pattern																				
Sensation																				
Mucus Description																				
Sex																				
Cervical Position																				

Cycle Day	1	2	3	4	5	6	7	8	9	10	11	12	13	14	15	16	17	18	19	20
Time																				
Luteal Phase Count																				
Temperature	.8	.8	.8	.8	.8	.8	.8	.8	.8	.8	.8	.8	.8	.8	.8	.8	.8	.8	.8	.8
	.7	.7	.7	.7	.7	.7	.7	.7	.7	.7	.7	.7	.7	.7	.7	.7	.7	.7	.7	.7
	.6	.6	.6	.6	.6	.6	.6	.6	.6	.6	.6	.6	.6	.6	.6	.6	.6	.6	.6	.6
	.5	.5	.5	.5	.5	.5	.5	.5	.5	.5	.5	.5	.5	.5	.5	.5	.5	.5	.5	.5
98°	.4	.4	.4	.4	.4	.4	.4	.4	.4	.4	.4	.4	.4	.4	.4	.4	.4	.4	.4	.4
	.3	.3	.3	.3	.3	.3	.3	.3	.3	.3	.3	.3	.3	.3	.3	.3	.3	.3	.3	.3
	.2	.2	.2	.2	.2	.2	.2	.2	.2	.2	.2	.2	.2	.2	.2	.2	.2	.2	.2	.2
	.1	.1	.1	.1	.1	.1	.1	.1	.1	.1	.1	.1	.1	.1	.1	.1	.1	.1	.1	.1
	.0	.0	.0	.0	.0	.0	.0	.0	.0	.0	.0	.0	.0	.0	.0	.0	.0	.0	.0	.0
	.9	.9	.9	.9	.9	.9	.9	.9	.9	.9	.9	.9	.9	.9	.9	.9	.9	.9	.9	.9
	.8	.8	.8	.8	.8	.8	.8	.8	.8	.8	.8	.8	.8	.8	.8	.8	.8	.8	.8	.8
	.7	.7	.7	.7	.7	.7	.7	.7	.7	.7	.7	.7	.7	.7	.7	.7	.7	.7	.7	.7
	.6	.6	.6	.6	.6	.6	.6	.6	.6	.6	.6	.6	.6	.6	.6	.6	.6	.6	.6	.6
97°	.5	.5	.5	.5	.5	.5	.5	.5	.5	.5	.5	.5	.5	.5	.5	.5	.5	.5	.5	.5
	.4	.4	.4	.4	.4	.4	.4	.4	.4	.4	.4	.4	.4	.4	.4	.4	.4	.4	.4	.4
	.3	.3	.3	.3	.3	.3	.3	.3	.3	.3	.3	.3	.3	.3	.3	.3	.3	.3	.3	.3
	.2	.2	.2	.2	.2	.2	.2	.2	.2	.2	.2	.2	.2	.2	.2	.2	.2	.2	.2	.2
	.1	.1	.1	.1	.1	.1	.1	.1	.1	.1	.1	.1	.1	.1	.1	.1	.1	.1	.1	.1
	.0	.0	.0	.0	.0	.0	.0	.0	.0	.0	.0	.0	.0	.0	.0	.0	.0	.0	.0	.0

Luteal Phase: ________ **Ovulation:** __________

21	22	23	24	25	26	27	28	29	30	31	32	33	34	35

21	22	23	24	25	26	27	28	29	30	31	32	33	34	35
.8	.8	.8	.8	.8	.8	.8	.8	.8	.8	.8	.8	.8	.8	.8
.7	.7	.7	.7	.7	.7	.7	.7	.7	.7	.7	.7	.7	.7	.7
.6	.6	.6	.6	.6	.6	.6	.6	.6	.6	.6	.6	.6	.6	.6
.5	.5	.5	.5	.5	.5	.5	.5	.5	.5	.5	.5	.5	.5	.5
.4	.4	.4	.4	.4	.4	.4	.4	.4	.4	.4	.4	.4	.4	.4
.3	.3	.3	.3	.3	.3	.3	.3	.3	.3	.3	.3	.3	.3	.3
.2	.2	.2	.2	.2	.2	.2	.2	.2	.2	.2	.2	.2	.2	.2
.1	.1	.1	.1	.1	.1	.1	.1	.1	.1	.1	.1	.1	.1	.1
.0	.0	.0	.0	.0	.0	.0	.0	.0	.0	.0	.0	.0	.0	.0
.9	.9	.9	.9	.9	.9	.9	.9	.9	.9	.9	.9	.9	.9	.9
.8	.8	.8	.8	.8	.8	.8	.8	.8	.8	.8	.8	.8	.8	.8
.7	.7	.7	.7	.7	.7	.7	.7	.7	.7	.7	.7	.7	.7	.7
.6	.6	.6	.6	.6	.6	.6	.6	.6	.6	.6	.6	.6	.6	.6
.5	.5	.5	.5	.5	.5	.5	.5	.5	.5	.5	.5	.5	.5	.5
.4	.4	.4	.4	.4	.4	.4	.4	.4	.4	.4	.4	.4	.4	.4
.3	.3	.3	.3	.3	.3	.3	.3	.3	.3	.3	.3	.3	.3	.3
.2	.2	.2	.2	.2	.2	.2	.2	.2	.2	.2	.2	.2	.2	.2
.1	.1	.1	.1	.1	.1	.1	.1	.1	.1	.1	.1	.1	.1	.1
.0	.0	.0	.0	.0	.0	.0	.0	.0	.0	.0	.0	.0	.0	.0

Daily Notes

1 ____________________
2 ____________________
3 ____________________
4 ____________________
5 ____________________
6 ____________________
7 ____________________
8 ____________________
9 ____________________
10 ____________________
11 ____________________
12 ____________________
13 ____________________
14 ____________________
15 ____________________
16 ____________________
17 ____________________
18 ____________________
19 ____________________
20 ____________________
21 ____________________
22 ____________________
23 ____________________
24 ____________________
25 ____________________
26 ____________________
27 ____________________
28 ____________________
29 ____________________
30 ____________________
31 ____________________
32 ____________________
33 ____________________
34 ____________________
35 ____________________

Cycle: ___ Month(s): ___________ Year: _____ Length: ________

Cycle Day	1	2	3	4	5	6	7	8	9	10	11	12	13	14	15	16	17	18	19	20
Weekday																				
Date																				
Mucus Pattern																				
Sensation																				
Mucus Description																				
Sex																				
Cervical Position																				

Cycle Day	1	2	3	4	5	6	7	8	9	10	11	12	13	14	15	16	17	18	19	20
Time																				
Luteal Phase Count																				
Temperature	.8	.8	.8	.8	.8	.8	.8	.8	.8	.8	.8	.8	.8	.8	.8	.8	.8	.8	.8	.8
	.7	.7	.7	.7	.7	.7	.7	.7	.7	.7	.7	.7	.7	.7	.7	.7	.7	.7	.7	.7
	.6	.6	.6	.6	.6	.6	.6	.6	.6	.6	.6	.6	.6	.6	.6	.6	.6	.6	.6	.6
	.5	.5	.5	.5	.5	.5	.5	.5	.5	.5	.5	.5	.5	.5	.5	.5	.5	.5	.5	.5
98°	.4	.4	.4	.4	.4	.4	.4	.4	.4	.4	.4	.4	.4	.4	.4	.4	.4	.4	.4	.4
	.3	.3	.3	.3	.3	.3	.3	.3	.3	.3	.3	.3	.3	.3	.3	.3	.3	.3	.3	.3
	.2	.2	.2	.2	.2	.2	.2	.2	.2	.2	.2	.2	.2	.2	.2	.2	.2	.2	.2	.2
	.1	.1	.1	.1	.1	.1	.1	.1	.1	.1	.1	.1	.1	.1	.1	.1	.1	.1	.1	.1
	.0	.0	.0	.0	.0	.0	.0	.0	.0	.0	.0	.0	.0	.0	.0	.0	.0	.0	.0	.0
	.9	.9	.9	.9	.9	.9	.9	.9	.9	.9	.9	.9	.9	.9	.9	.9	.9	.9	.9	.9
	.8	.8	.8	.8	.8	.8	.8	.8	.8	.8	.8	.8	.8	.8	.8	.8	.8	.8	.8	.8
	.7	.7	.7	.7	.7	.7	.7	.7	.7	.7	.7	.7	.7	.7	.7	.7	.7	.7	.7	.7
	.6	.6	.6	.6	.6	.6	.6	.6	.6	.6	.6	.6	.6	.6	.6	.6	.6	.6	.6	.6
97°	.5	.5	.5	.5	.5	.5	.5	.5	.5	.5	.5	.5	.5	.5	.5	.5	.5	.5	.5	.5
	.4	.4	.4	.4	.4	.4	.4	.4	.4	.4	.4	.4	.4	.4	.4	.4	.4	.4	.4	.4
	.3	.3	.3	.3	.3	.3	.3	.3	.3	.3	.3	.3	.3	.3	.3	.3	.3	.3	.3	.3
	.2	.2	.2	.2	.2	.2	.2	.2	.2	.2	.2	.2	.2	.2	.2	.2	.2	.2	.2	.2
	.1	.1	.1	.1	.1	.1	.1	.1	.1	.1	.1	.1	.1	.1	.1	.1	.1	.1	.1	.1
	.0	.0	.0	.0	.0	.0	.0	.0	.0	.0	.0	.0	.0	.0	.0	.0	.0	.0	.0	.0

Luteal Phase: ________ **Ovulation:** __________

21	22	23	24	25	26	27	28	29	30	31	32	33	34	35

21	22	23	24	25	26	27	28	29	30	31	32	33	34	35
.8	.8	.8	.8	.8	.8	.8	.8	.8	.8	.8	.8	.8	.8	.8
.7	.7	.7	.7	.7	.7	.7	.7	.7	.7	.7	.7	.7	.7	.7
.6	.6	.6	.6	.6	.6	.6	.6	.6	.6	.6	.6	.6	.6	.6
.5	.5	.5	.5	.5	.5	.5	.5	.5	.5	.5	.5	.5	.5	.5
.4	.4	.4	.4	.4	.4	.4	.4	.4	.4	.4	.4	.4	.4	.4
.3	.3	.3	.3	.3	.3	.3	.3	.3	.3	.3	.3	.3	.3	.3
.2	.2	.2	.2	.2	.2	.2	.2	.2	.2	.2	.2	.2	.2	.2
.1	.1	.1	.1	.1	.1	.1	.1	.1	.1	.1	.1	.1	.1	.1
.0	.0	.0	.0	.0	.0	.0	.0	.0	.0	.0	.0	.0	.0	.0
.9	.9	.9	.9	.9	.9	.9	.9	.9	.9	.9	.9	.9	.9	.9
.8	.8	.8	.8	.8	.8	.8	.8	.8	.8	.8	.8	.8	.8	.8
.7	.7	.7	.7	.7	.7	.7	.7	.7	.7	.7	.7	.7	.7	.7
.6	.6	.6	.6	.6	.6	.6	.6	.6	.6	.6	.6	.6	.6	.6
.5	.5	.5	.5	.5	.5	.5	.5	.5	.5	.5	.5	.5	.5	.5
.4	.4	.4	.4	.4	.4	.4	.4	.4	.4	.4	.4	.4	.4	.4
.3	.3	.3	.3	.3	.3	.3	.3	.3	.3	.3	.3	.3	.3	.3
.2	.2	.2	.2	.2	.2	.2	.2	.2	.2	.2	.2	.2	.2	.2
.1	.1	.1	.1	.1	.1	.1	.1	.1	.1	.1	.1	.1	.1	.1
.0	.0	.0	.0	.0	.0	.0	.0	.0	.0	.0	.0	.0	.0	.0

Daily Notes

1 ______
2 ______
3 ______
4 ______
5 ______
6 ______
7 ______
8 ______
9 ______
10 ______
11 ______
12 ______
13 ______
14 ______
15 ______
16 ______
17 ______
18 ______
19 ______
20 ______
21 ______
22 ______
23 ______
24 ______
25 ______
26 ______
27 ______
28 ______
29 ______
30 ______
31 ______
32 ______
33 ______
34 ______
35 ______

Cycle: ___ **Month(s):** ___________ **Year:** _____ **Length:** ________

Cycle Day	1	2	3	4	5	6	7	8	9	10	11	12	13	14	15	16	17	18	19	20
Weekday																				
Date																				
Mucus Pattern																				
Sensation																				
Mucus Description																				
Sex																				
Cervical Position																				

Cycle Day	1	2	3	4	5	6	7	8	9	10	11	12	13	14	15	16	17	18	19	20
Time																				
Luteal Phase Count																				
Temperature	.8	.8	.8	.8	.8	.8	.8	.8	.8	.8	.8	.8	.8	.8	.8	.8	.8	.8	.8	.8
	.7	.7	.7	.7	.7	.7	.7	.7	.7	.7	.7	.7	.7	.7	.7	.7	.7	.7	.7	.7
	.6	.6	.6	.6	.6	.6	.6	.6	.6	.6	.6	.6	.6	.6	.6	.6	.6	.6	.6	.6
	.5	.5	.5	.5	.5	.5	.5	.5	.5	.5	.5	.5	.5	.5	.5	.5	.5	.5	.5	.5
98°	.4	.4	.4	.4	.4	.4	.4	.4	.4	.4	.4	.4	.4	.4	.4	.4	.4	.4	.4	.4
	.3	.3	.3	.3	.3	.3	.3	.3	.3	.3	.3	.3	.3	.3	.3	.3	.3	.3	.3	.3
	.2	.2	.2	.2	.2	.2	.2	.2	.2	.2	.2	.2	.2	.2	.2	.2	.2	.2	.2	.2
	.1	.1	.1	.1	.1	.1	.1	.1	.1	.1	.1	.1	.1	.1	.1	.1	.1	.1	.1	.1
	.0	.0	.0	.0	.0	.0	.0	.0	.0	.0	.0	.0	.0	.0	.0	.0	.0	.0	.0	.0
	.9	.9	.9	.9	.9	.9	.9	.9	.9	.9	.9	.9	.9	.9	.9	.9	.9	.9	.9	.9
	.8	.8	.8	.8	.8	.8	.8	.8	.8	.8	.8	.8	.8	.8	.8	.8	.8	.8	.8	.8
	.7	.7	.7	.7	.7	.7	.7	.7	.7	.7	.7	.7	.7	.7	.7	.7	.7	.7	.7	.7
	.6	.6	.6	.6	.6	.6	.6	.6	.6	.6	.6	.6	.6	.6	.6	.6	.6	.6	.6	.6
97°	.5	.5	.5	.5	.5	.5	.5	.5	.5	.5	.5	.5	.5	.5	.5	.5	.5	.5	.5	.5
	.4	.4	.4	.4	.4	.4	.4	.4	.4	.4	.4	.4	.4	.4	.4	.4	.4	.4	.4	.4
	.3	.3	.3	.3	.3	.3	.3	.3	.3	.3	.3	.3	.3	.3	.3	.3	.3	.3	.3	.3
	.2	.2	.2	.2	.2	.2	.2	.2	.2	.2	.2	.2	.2	.2	.2	.2	.2	.2	.2	.2
	.1	.1	.1	.1	.1	.1	.1	.1	.1	.1	.1	.1	.1	.1	.1	.1	.1	.1	.1	.1
	.0	.0	.0	.0	.0	.0	.0	.0	.0	.0	.0	.0	.0	.0	.0	.0	.0	.0	.0	.0

Luteal Phase: __________ **Ovulation:** __________

21	22	23	24	25	26	27	28	29	30	31	32	33	34	35

21	22	23	24	25	26	27	28	29	30	31	32	33	34	35
.8	.8	.8	.8	.8	.8	.8	.8	.8	.8	.8	.8	.8	.8	.8
.7	.7	.7	.7	.7	.7	.7	.7	.7	.7	.7	.7	.7	.7	.7
.6	.6	.6	.6	.6	.6	.6	.6	.6	.6	.6	.6	.6	.6	.6
.5	.5	.5	.5	.5	.5	.5	.5	.5	.5	.5	.5	.5	.5	.5
.4	.4	.4	.4	.4	.4	.4	.4	.4	.4	.4	.4	.4	.4	.4
.3	.3	.3	.3	.3	.3	.3	.3	.3	.3	.3	.3	.3	.3	.3
.2	.2	.2	.2	.2	.2	.2	.2	.2	.2	.2	.2	.2	.2	.2
.1	.1	.1	.1	.1	.1	.1	.1	.1	.1	.1	.1	.1	.1	.1
.0	.0	.0	.0	.0	.0	.0	.0	.0	.0	.0	.0	.0	.0	.0
.9	.9	.9	.9	.9	.9	.9	.9	.9	.9	.9	.9	.9	.9	.9
.8	.8	.8	.8	.8	.8	.8	.8	.8	.8	.8	.8	.8	.8	.8
.7	.7	.7	.7	.7	.7	.7	.7	.7	.7	.7	.7	.7	.7	.7
.6	.6	.6	.6	.6	.6	.6	.6	.6	.6	.6	.6	.6	.6	.6
.5	.5	.5	.5	.5	.5	.5	.5	.5	.5	.5	.5	.5	.5	.5
.4	.4	.4	.4	.4	.4	.4	.4	.4	.4	.4	.4	.4	.4	.4
.3	.3	.3	.3	.3	.3	.3	.3	.3	.3	.3	.3	.3	.3	.3
.2	.2	.2	.2	.2	.2	.2	.2	.2	.2	.2	.2	.2	.2	.2
.1	.1	.1	.1	.1	.1	.1	.1	.1	.1	.1	.1	.1	.1	.1
.0	.0	.0	.0	.0	.0	.0	.0	.0	.0	.0	.0	.0	.0	.0

Daily Notes

1 ____________________
2 ____________________
3 ____________________
4 ____________________
5 ____________________
6 ____________________
7 ____________________
8 ____________________
9 ____________________
10 ____________________
11 ____________________
12 ____________________
13 ____________________
14 ____________________
15 ____________________
16 ____________________
17 ____________________
18 ____________________
19 ____________________
20 ____________________
21 ____________________
22 ____________________
23 ____________________
24 ____________________
25 ____________________
26 ____________________
27 ____________________
28 ____________________
29 ____________________
30 ____________________
31 ____________________
32 ____________________
33 ____________________
34 ____________________
35 ____________________

Cycle: ____ Month(s): ____________ Year: ______ Length: _________

Cycle Day	1	2	3	4	5	6	7	8	9	10	11	12	13	14	15	16	17	18	19	20
Weekday																				
Date																				
Mucus Pattern																				
Sensation																				
Mucus Description																				
Sex																				
Cervical Position																				

Cycle Day	1	2	3	4	5	6	7	8	9	10	11	12	13	14	15	16	17	18	19	20
Time																				
Luteal Phase Count																				
Temperature	.8	.8	.8	.8	.8	.8	.8	.8	.8	.8	.8	.8	.8	.8	.8	.8	.8	.8	.8	.8
	.7	.7	.7	.7	.7	.7	.7	.7	.7	.7	.7	.7	.7	.7	.7	.7	.7	.7	.7	.7
	.6	.6	.6	.6	.6	.6	.6	.6	.6	.6	.6	.6	.6	.6	.6	.6	.6	.6	.6	.6
	.5	.5	.5	.5	.5	.5	.5	.5	.5	.5	.5	.5	.5	.5	.5	.5	.5	.5	.5	.5
98°	.4	.4	.4	.4	.4	.4	.4	.4	.4	.4	.4	.4	.4	.4	.4	.4	.4	.4	.4	.4
	.3	.3	.3	.3	.3	.3	.3	.3	.3	.3	.3	.3	.3	.3	.3	.3	.3	.3	.3	.3
	.2	.2	.2	.2	.2	.2	.2	.2	.2	.2	.2	.2	.2	.2	.2	.2	.2	.2	.2	.2
	.1	.1	.1	.1	.1	.1	.1	.1	.1	.1	.1	.1	.1	.1	.1	.1	.1	.1	.1	.1
	.0	.0	.0	.0	.0	.0	.0	.0	.0	.0	.0	.0	.0	.0	.0	.0	.0	.0	.0	.0
	.9	.9	.9	.9	.9	.9	.9	.9	.9	.9	.9	.9	.9	.9	.9	.9	.9	.9	.9	.9
	.8	.8	.8	.8	.8	.8	.8	.8	.8	.8	.8	.8	.8	.8	.8	.8	.8	.8	.8	.8
	.7	.7	.7	.7	.7	.7	.7	.7	.7	.7	.7	.7	.7	.7	.7	.7	.7	.7	.7	.7
	.6	.6	.6	.6	.6	.6	.6	.6	.6	.6	.6	.6	.6	.6	.6	.6	.6	.6	.6	.6
97°	.5	.5	.5	.5	.5	.5	.5	.5	.5	.5	.5	.5	.5	.5	.5	.5	.5	.5	.5	.5
	.4	.4	.4	.4	.4	.4	.4	.4	.4	.4	.4	.4	.4	.4	.4	.4	.4	.4	.4	.4
	.3	.3	.3	.3	.3	.3	.3	.3	.3	.3	.3	.3	.3	.3	.3	.3	.3	.3	.3	.3
	.2	.2	.2	.2	.2	.2	.2	.2	.2	.2	.2	.2	.2	.2	.2	.2	.2	.2	.2	.2
	.1	.1	.1	.1	.1	.1	.1	.1	.1	.1	.1	.1	.1	.1	.1	.1	.1	.1	.1	.1
	.0	.0	.0	.0	.0	.0	.0	.0	.0	.0	.0	.0	.0	.0	.0	.0	.0	.0	.0	.0

Luteal Phase: ________ **Ovulation:** __________

21	22	23	24	25	26	27	28	29	30	31	32	33	34	35

21	22	23	24	25	26	27	28	29	30	31	32	33	34	35
.8	.8	.8	.8	.8	.8	.8	.8	.8	.8	.8	.8	.8	.8	.8
.7	.7	.7	.7	.7	.7	.7	.7	.7	.7	.7	.7	.7	.7	.7
.6	.6	.6	.6	.6	.6	.6	.6	.6	.6	.6	.6	.6	.6	.6
.5	.5	.5	.5	.5	.5	.5	.5	.5	.5	.5	.5	.5	.5	.5
.4	.4	.4	.4	.4	.4	.4	.4	.4	.4	.4	.4	.4	.4	.4
.3	.3	.3	.3	.3	.3	.3	.3	.3	.3	.3	.3	.3	.3	.3
.2	.2	.2	.2	.2	.2	.2	.2	.2	.2	.2	.2	.2	.2	.2
.1	.1	.1	.1	.1	.1	.1	.1	.1	.1	.1	.1	.1	.1	.1
.0	.0	.0	.0	.0	.0	.0	.0	.0	.0	.0	.0	.0	.0	.0
.9	.9	.9	.9	.9	.9	.9	.9	.9	.9	.9	.9	.9	.9	.9
.8	.8	.8	.8	.8	.8	.8	.8	.8	.8	.8	.8	.8	.8	.8
.7	.7	.7	.7	.7	.7	.7	.7	.7	.7	.7	.7	.7	.7	.7
.6	.6	.6	.6	.6	.6	.6	.6	.6	.6	.6	.6	.6	.6	.6
.5	.5	.5	.5	.5	.5	.5	.5	.5	.5	.5	.5	.5	.5	.5
.4	.4	.4	.4	.4	.4	.4	.4	.4	.4	.4	.4	.4	.4	.4
.3	.3	.3	.3	.3	.3	.3	.3	.3	.3	.3	.3	.3	.3	.3
.2	.2	.2	.2	.2	.2	.2	.2	.2	.2	.2	.2	.2	.2	.2
.1	.1	.1	.1	.1	.1	.1	.1	.1	.1	.1	.1	.1	.1	.1
.0	.0	.0	.0	.0	.0	.0	.0	.0	.0	.0	.0	.0	.0	.0

Daily Notes

1 ____________________
2 ____________________
3 ____________________
4 ____________________
5 ____________________
6 ____________________
7 ____________________
8 ____________________
9 ____________________
10 ____________________
11 ____________________
12 ____________________
13 ____________________
14 ____________________
15 ____________________
16 ____________________
17 ____________________
18 ____________________
19 ____________________
20 ____________________
21 ____________________
22 ____________________
23 ____________________
24 ____________________
25 ____________________
26 ____________________
27 ____________________
28 ____________________
29 ____________________
30 ____________________
31 ____________________
32 ____________________
33 ____________________
34 ____________________
35 ____________________

Cycle: ___ Month(s): ___________ Year: _____ Length: ________

Cycle Day	1	2	3	4	5	6	7	8	9	10	11	12	13	14	15	16	17	18	19	20
Weekday																				
Date																				
Mucus Pattern																				
Sensation																				
Mucus Description																				
Sex																				
Cervical Position																				

Cycle Day	1	2	3	4	5	6	7	8	9	10	11	12	13	14	15	16	17	18	19	20
Time																				
Luteal Phase Count																				
Temperature	.8	.8	.8	.8	.8	.8	.8	.8	.8	.8	.8	.8	.8	.8	.8	.8	.8	.8	.8	.8
	.7	.7	.7	.7	.7	.7	.7	.7	.7	.7	.7	.7	.7	.7	.7	.7	.7	.7	.7	.7
	.6	.6	.6	.6	.6	.6	.6	.6	.6	.6	.6	.6	.6	.6	.6	.6	.6	.6	.6	.6
	.5	.5	.5	.5	.5	.5	.5	.5	.5	.5	.5	.5	.5	.5	.5	.5	.5	.5	.5	.5
98°	.4	.4	.4	.4	.4	.4	.4	.4	.4	.4	.4	.4	.4	.4	.4	.4	.4	.4	.4	.4
	.3	.3	.3	.3	.3	.3	.3	.3	.3	.3	.3	.3	.3	.3	.3	.3	.3	.3	.3	.3
	.2	.2	.2	.2	.2	.2	.2	.2	.2	.2	.2	.2	.2	.2	.2	.2	.2	.2	.2	.2
	.1	.1	.1	.1	.1	.1	.1	.1	.1	.1	.1	.1	.1	.1	.1	.1	.1	.1	.1	.1
	.0	.0	.0	.0	.0	.0	.0	.0	.0	.0	.0	.0	.0	.0	.0	.0	.0	.0	.0	.0
	.9	.9	.9	.9	.9	.9	.9	.9	.9	.9	.9	.9	.9	.9	.9	.9	.9	.9	.9	.9
	.8	.8	.8	.8	.8	.8	.8	.8	.8	.8	.8	.8	.8	.8	.8	.8	.8	.8	.8	.8
	.7	.7	.7	.7	.7	.7	.7	.7	.7	.7	.7	.7	.7	.7	.7	.7	.7	.7	.7	.7
	.6	.6	.6	.6	.6	.6	.6	.6	.6	.6	.6	.6	.6	.6	.6	.6	.6	.6	.6	.6
97°	.5	.5	.5	.5	.5	.5	.5	.5	.5	.5	.5	.5	.5	.5	.5	.5	.5	.5	.5	.5
	.4	.4	.4	.4	.4	.4	.4	.4	.4	.4	.4	.4	.4	.4	.4	.4	.4	.4	.4	.4
	.3	.3	.3	.3	.3	.3	.3	.3	.3	.3	.3	.3	.3	.3	.3	.3	.3	.3	.3	.3
	.2	.2	.2	.2	.2	.2	.2	.2	.2	.2	.2	.2	.2	.2	.2	.2	.2	.2	.2	.2
	.1	.1	.1	.1	.1	.1	.1	.1	.1	.1	.1	.1	.1	.1	.1	.1	.1	.1	.1	.1
	.0	.0	.0	.0	.0	.0	.0	.0	.0	.0	.0	.0	.0	.0	.0	.0	.0	.0	.0	.0

Luteal Phase: ________ **Ovulation:** __________

21	22	23	24	25	26	27	28	29	30	31	32	33	34	35

21	22	23	24	25	26	27	28	29	30	31	32	33	34	35
.8	.8	.8	.8	.8	.8	.8	.8	.8	.8	.8	.8	.8	.8	.8
.7	.7	.7	.7	.7	.7	.7	.7	.7	.7	.7	.7	.7	.7	.7
.6	.6	.6	.6	.6	.6	.6	.6	.6	.6	.6	.6	.6	.6	.6
.5	.5	.5	.5	.5	.5	.5	.5	.5	.5	.5	.5	.5	.5	.5
.4	.4	.4	.4	.4	.4	.4	.4	.4	.4	.4	.4	.4	.4	.4
.3	.3	.3	.3	.3	.3	.3	.3	.3	.3	.3	.3	.3	.3	.3
.2	.2	.2	.2	.2	.2	.2	.2	.2	.2	.2	.2	.2	.2	.2
.1	.1	.1	.1	.1	.1	.1	.1	.1	.1	.1	.1	.1	.1	.1
.0	.0	.0	.0	.0	.0	.0	.0	.0	.0	.0	.0	.0	.0	.0
.9	.9	.9	.9	.9	.9	.9	.9	.9	.9	.9	.9	.9	.9	.9
.8	.8	.8	.8	.8	.8	.8	.8	.8	.8	.8	.8	.8	.8	.8
.7	.7	.7	.7	.7	.7	.7	.7	.7	.7	.7	.7	.7	.7	.7
.6	.6	.6	.6	.6	.6	.6	.6	.6	.6	.6	.6	.6	.6	.6
.5	.5	.5	.5	.5	.5	.5	.5	.5	.5	.5	.5	.5	.5	.5
.4	.4	.4	.4	.4	.4	.4	.4	.4	.4	.4	.4	.4	.4	.4
.3	.3	.3	.3	.3	.3	.3	.3	.3	.3	.3	.3	.3	.3	.3
.2	.2	.2	.2	.2	.2	.2	.2	.2	.2	.2	.2	.2	.2	.2
.1	.1	.1	.1	.1	.1	.1	.1	.1	.1	.1	.1	.1	.1	.1
.0	.0	.0	.0	.0	.0	.0	.0	.0	.0	.0	.0	.0	.0	.0

Daily Notes

1 ______
2 ______
3 ______
4 ______
5 ______
6 ______
7 ______
8 ______
9 ______
10 ______
11 ______
12 ______
13 ______
14 ______
15 ______
16 ______
17 ______
18 ______
19 ______
20 ______
21 ______
22 ______
23 ______
24 ______
25 ______
26 ______
27 ______
28 ______
29 ______
30 ______
31 ______
32 ______
33 ______
34 ______
35 ______

Cycle: ____ **Month(s):** ____________ **Year:** ______ **Length:** ________

Cycle Day	1	2	3	4	5	6	7	8	9	10	11	12	13	14	15	16	17	18	19	20
Weekday																				
Date																				
Mucus Pattern																				
Sensation																				
Mucus Description																				
Sex																				
Cervical Position																				

Cycle Day	1	2	3	4	5	6	7	8	9	10	11	12	13	14	15	16	17	18	19	20
Time																				
Luteal Phase Count																				
Temperature	.8	.8	.8	.8	.8	.8	.8	.8	.8	.8	.8	.8	.8	.8	.8	.8	.8	.8	.8	.8
	.7	.7	.7	.7	.7	.7	.7	.7	.7	.7	.7	.7	.7	.7	.7	.7	.7	.7	.7	.7
	.6	.6	.6	.6	.6	.6	.6	.6	.6	.6	.6	.6	.6	.6	.6	.6	.6	.6	.6	.6
	.5	.5	.5	.5	.5	.5	.5	.5	.5	.5	.5	.5	.5	.5	.5	.5	.5	.5	.5	.5
98°	.4	.4	.4	.4	.4	.4	.4	.4	.4	.4	.4	.4	.4	.4	.4	.4	.4	.4	.4	.4
	.3	.3	.3	.3	.3	.3	.3	.3	.3	.3	.3	.3	.3	.3	.3	.3	.3	.3	.3	.3
	.2	.2	.2	.2	.2	.2	.2	.2	.2	.2	.2	.2	.2	.2	.2	.2	.2	.2	.2	.2
	.1	.1	.1	.1	.1	.1	.1	.1	.1	.1	.1	.1	.1	.1	.1	.1	.1	.1	.1	.1
	.0	.0	.0	.0	.0	.0	.0	.0	.0	.0	.0	.0	.0	.0	.0	.0	.0	.0	.0	.0
	.9	.9	.9	.9	.9	.9	.9	.9	.9	.9	.9	.9	.9	.9	.9	.9	.9	.9	.9	.9
	.8	.8	.8	.8	.8	.8	.8	.8	.8	.8	.8	.8	.8	.8	.8	.8	.8	.8	.8	.8
	.7	.7	.7	.7	.7	.7	.7	.7	.7	.7	.7	.7	.7	.7	.7	.7	.7	.7	.7	.7
	.6	.6	.6	.6	.6	.6	.6	.6	.6	.6	.6	.6	.6	.6	.6	.6	.6	.6	.6	.6
97°	.5	.5	.5	.5	.5	.5	.5	.5	.5	.5	.5	.5	.5	.5	.5	.5	.5	.5	.5	.5
	.4	.4	.4	.4	.4	.4	.4	.4	.4	.4	.4	.4	.4	.4	.4	.4	.4	.4	.4	.4
	.3	.3	.3	.3	.3	.3	.3	.3	.3	.3	.3	.3	.3	.3	.3	.3	.3	.3	.3	.3
	.2	.2	.2	.2	.2	.2	.2	.2	.2	.2	.2	.2	.2	.2	.2	.2	.2	.2	.2	.2
	.1	.1	.1	.1	.1	.1	.1	.1	.1	.1	.1	.1	.1	.1	.1	.1	.1	.1	.1	.1
	.0	.0	.0	.0	.0	.0	.0	.0	.0	.0	.0	.0	.0	.0	.0	.0	.0	.0	.0	.0

Luteal Phase: __________ **Ovulation:** ____________

21 22 23 24 25 26 27 28 29 30 31 32 33 34 35

21 22 23 24 25 26 27 28 29 30 31 32 33 34 35

21	22	23	24	25	26	27	28	29	30	31	32	33	34	35
.8	.8	.8	.8	.8	.8	.8	.8	.8	.8	.8	.8	.8	.8	.8
.7	.7	.7	.7	.7	.7	.7	.7	.7	.7	.7	.7	.7	.7	.7
.6	.6	.6	.6	.6	.6	.6	.6	.6	.6	.6	.6	.6	.6	.6
.5	.5	.5	.5	.5	.5	.5	.5	.5	.5	.5	.5	.5	.5	.5
.4	.4	.4	.4	.4	.4	.4	.4	.4	.4	.4	.4	.4	.4	.4
.3	.3	.3	.3	.3	.3	.3	.3	.3	.3	.3	.3	.3	.3	.3
.2	.2	.2	.2	.2	.2	.2	.2	.2	.2	.2	.2	.2	.2	.2
.1	.1	.1	.1	.1	.1	.1	.1	.1	.1	.1	.1	.1	.1	.1
.0	.0	.0	.0	.0	.0	.0	.0	.0	.0	.0	.0	.0	.0	.0
.9	.9	.9	.9	.9	.9	.9	.9	.9	.9	.9	.9	.9	.9	.9
.8	.8	.8	.8	.8	.8	.8	.8	.8	.8	.8	.8	.8	.8	.8
.7	.7	.7	.7	.7	.7	.7	.7	.7	.7	.7	.7	.7	.7	.7
.6	.6	.6	.6	.6	.6	.6	.6	.6	.6	.6	.6	.6	.6	.6
.5	.5	.5	.5	.5	.5	.5	.5	.5	.5	.5	.5	.5	.5	.5
.4	.4	.4	.4	.4	.4	.4	.4	.4	.4	.4	.4	.4	.4	.4
.3	.3	.3	.3	.3	.3	.3	.3	.3	.3	.3	.3	.3	.3	.3
.2	.2	.2	.2	.2	.2	.2	.2	.2	.2	.2	.2	.2	.2	.2
.1	.1	.1	.1	.1	.1	.1	.1	.1	.1	.1	.1	.1	.1	.1
.0	.0	.0	.0	.0	.0	.0	.0	.0	.0	.0	.0	.0	.0	.0

Daily Notes

1 ______
2 ______
3 ______
4 ______
5 ______
6 ______
7 ______
8 ______
9 ______
10 ______
11 ______
12 ______
13 ______
14 ______
15 ______
16 ______
17 ______
18 ______
19 ______
20 ______
21 ______
22 ______
23 ______
24 ______
25 ______
26 ______
27 ______
28 ______
29 ______
30 ______
31 ______
32 ______
33 ______
34 ______
35 ______

Cycle: ___ Month(s): ___________ Year: _____ Length: ________

Cycle Day	1	2	3	4	5	6	7	8	9	10	11	12	13	14	15	16	17	18	19	20
Weekday																				
Date																				
Mucus Pattern																				
Sensation																				
Mucus Description																				
Sex																				
Cervical Position																				

Cycle Day	1	2	3	4	5	6	7	8	9	10	11	12	13	14	15	16	17	18	19	20
Time																				
Luteal Phase Count																				
Temperature	.8	.8	.8	.8	.8	.8	.8	.8	.8	.8	.8	.8	.8	.8	.8	.8	.8	.8	.8	.8
	.7	.7	.7	.7	.7	.7	.7	.7	.7	.7	.7	.7	.7	.7	.7	.7	.7	.7	.7	.7
	.6	.6	.6	.6	.6	.6	.6	.6	.6	.6	.6	.6	.6	.6	.6	.6	.6	.6	.6	.6
	.5	.5	.5	.5	.5	.5	.5	.5	.5	.5	.5	.5	.5	.5	.5	.5	.5	.5	.5	.5
98°	.4	.4	.4	.4	.4	.4	.4	.4	.4	.4	.4	.4	.4	.4	.4	.4	.4	.4	.4	.4
	.3	.3	.3	.3	.3	.3	.3	.3	.3	.3	.3	.3	.3	.3	.3	.3	.3	.3	.3	.3
	.2	.2	.2	.2	.2	.2	.2	.2	.2	.2	.2	.2	.2	.2	.2	.2	.2	.2	.2	.2
	.1	.1	.1	.1	.1	.1	.1	.1	.1	.1	.1	.1	.1	.1	.1	.1	.1	.1	.1	.1
	.0	.0	.0	.0	.0	.0	.0	.0	.0	.0	.0	.0	.0	.0	.0	.0	.0	.0	.0	.0
	.9	.9	.9	.9	.9	.9	.9	.9	.9	.9	.9	.9	.9	.9	.9	.9	.9	.9	.9	.9
	.8	.8	.8	.8	.8	.8	.8	.8	.8	.8	.8	.8	.8	.8	.8	.8	.8	.8	.8	.8
	.7	.7	.7	.7	.7	.7	.7	.7	.7	.7	.7	.7	.7	.7	.7	.7	.7	.7	.7	.7
	.6	.6	.6	.6	.6	.6	.6	.6	.6	.6	.6	.6	.6	.6	.6	.6	.6	.6	.6	.6
97°	.5	.5	.5	.5	.5	.5	.5	.5	.5	.5	.5	.5	.5	.5	.5	.5	.5	.5	.5	.5
	.4	.4	.4	.4	.4	.4	.4	.4	.4	.4	.4	.4	.4	.4	.4	.4	.4	.4	.4	.4
	.3	.3	.3	.3	.3	.3	.3	.3	.3	.3	.3	.3	.3	.3	.3	.3	.3	.3	.3	.3
	.2	.2	.2	.2	.2	.2	.2	.2	.2	.2	.2	.2	.2	.2	.2	.2	.2	.2	.2	.2
	.1	.1	.1	.1	.1	.1	.1	.1	.1	.1	.1	.1	.1	.1	.1	.1	.1	.1	.1	.1
	.0	.0	.0	.0	.0	.0	.0	.0	.0	.0	.0	.0	.0	.0	.0	.0	.0	.0	.0	.0

Luteal Phase: ________ **Ovulation:** __________

21	22	23	24	25	26	27	28	29	30	31	32	33	34	35
○	○	○	○	○	○	○	○	○	○	○	○	○	○	○
○	○	○	○	○	○	○	○	○	○	○	○	○	○	○

21	22	23	24	25	26	27	28	29	30	31	32	33	34	35
.8	.8	.8	.8	.8	.8	.8	.8	.8	.8	.8	.8	.8	.8	.8
.7	.7	.7	.7	.7	.7	.7	.7	.7	.7	.7	.7	.7	.7	.7
.6	.6	.6	.6	.6	.6	.6	.6	.6	.6	.6	.6	.6	.6	.6
.5	.5	.5	.5	.5	.5	.5	.5	.5	.5	.5	.5	.5	.5	.5
.4	.4	.4	.4	.4	.4	.4	.4	.4	.4	.4	.4	.4	.4	.4
.3	.3	.3	.3	.3	.3	.3	.3	.3	.3	.3	.3	.3	.3	.3
.2	.2	.2	2	.2	.2	.2	.2	.2	.2	.2	.2	.2	.2	.2
.1	.1	.1	.1	.1	.1	.1	.1	.1	.1	.1	.1	.1	.1	.1
.0	.0	.0	.0	.0	.0	.0	.0	.0	.0	.0	.0	.0	.0	.0
.9	.9	.9	.9	.9	.9	.9	.9	.9	.9	.9	.9	.9	.9	.9
.8	.8	.8	.8	.8	.8	.8	.8	.8	.8	.8	.8	.8	.8	.8
.7	.7	.7	.7	.7	.7	.7	.7	.7	.7	.7	.7	.7	.7	.7
.6	.6	.6	.6	.6	.6	.6	.6	.6	.6	.6	.6	.6	.6	.6
.5	.5	.5	.5	.5	.5	.5	.5	.5	.5	.5	.5	.5	.5	.5
.4	.4	.4	.4	.4	.4	.4	.4	.4	.4	.4	.4	.4	.4	.4
.3	.3	.3	.3	.3	.3	.3	.3	.3	.3	.3	.3	.3	.3	.3
.2	.2	.2	.2	.2	.2	.2	.2	.2	.2	.2	.2	.2	.2	.2
.1	.1	.1	.1	.1	.1	.1	.1	.1	.1	.1	.1	.1	.1	.1
.0	.0	.0	.0	.0	.0	.0	.0	.0	.0	.0	.0	.0	.0	.0

Daily Notes

1 ______________________
2 ______________________
3 ______________________
4 ______________________
5 ______________________
6 ______________________
7 ______________________
8 ______________________
9 ______________________
10 ______________________
11 ______________________
12 ______________________
13 ______________________
14 ______________________
15 ______________________
16 ______________________
17 ______________________
18 ______________________
19 ______________________
20 ______________________
21 ______________________
22 ______________________
23 ______________________
24 ______________________
25 ______________________
26 ______________________
27 ______________________
28 ______________________
29 ______________________
30 ______________________
31 ______________________
32 ______________________
33 ______________________
34 ______________________
35 ______________________

Cycle: ____ Month(s): ____________ Year: ______ Length: ________

Cycle Day	1	2	3	4	5	6	7	8	9	10	11	12	13	14	15	16	17	18	19	20
Weekday																				
Date																				
Mucus Pattern																				
Sensation																				
Mucus Description																				
Sex																				
Cervical Position																				

Cycle Day	1	2	3	4	5	6	7	8	9	10	11	12	13	14	15	16	17	18	19	20
Time																				
Luteal Phase Count																				
Temperature	.8	.8	.8	.8	.8	.8	.8	.8	.8	.8	.8	.8	.8	.8	.8	.8	.8	.8	.8	.8
	.7	.7	.7	.7	.7	.7	.7	.7	.7	.7	.7	.7	.7	.7	.7	.7	.7	.7	.7	.7
	.6	.6	.6	.6	.6	.6	.6	.6	.6	.6	.6	.6	.6	.6	.6	.6	.6	.6	.6	.6
	.5	.5	.5	.5	.5	.5	.5	.5	.5	.5	.5	.5	.5	.5	.5	.5	.5	.5	.5	.5
98°	.4	.4	.4	.4	.4	.4	.4	.4	.4	.4	.4	.4	.4	.4	.4	.4	.4	.4	.4	.4
	.3	.3	.3	.3	.3	.3	.3	.3	.3	.3	.3	.3	.3	.3	.3	.3	.3	.3	.3	.3
	.2	.2	.2	.2	.2	.2	.2	.2	.2	.2	.2	.2	.2	.2	.2	.2	.2	.2	.2	.2
	.1	.1	.1	.1	.1	.1	.1	.1	.1	.1	.1	.1	.1	.1	.1	.1	.1	.1	.1	.1
	.0	.0	.0	.0	.0	.0	.0	.0	.0	.0	.0	.0	.0	.0	.0	.0	.0	.0	.0	.0
	.9	.9	.9	.9	.9	.9	.9	.9	.9	.9	.9	.9	.9	.9	.9	.9	.9	.9	.9	.9
	.8	.8	.8	.8	.8	.8	.8	.8	.8	.8	.8	.8	.8	.8	.8	.8	.8	.8	.8	.8
	.7	.7	.7	.7	.7	.7	.7	.7	.7	.7	.7	.7	.7	.7	.7	.7	.7	.7	.7	.7
	.6	.6	.6	.6	.6	.6	.6	.6	.6	.6	.6	.6	.6	.6	.6	.6	.6	.6	.6	.6
97°	.5	.5	.5	.5	.5	.5	.5	.5	.5	.5	.5	.5	.5	.5	.5	.5	.5	.5	.5	.5
	.4	.4	.4	.4	.4	.4	.4	.4	.4	.4	.4	.4	.4	.4	.4	.4	.4	.4	.4	.4
	.3	.3	.3	.3	.3	.3	.3	.3	.3	.3	.3	.3	.3	.3	.3	.3	.3	.3	.3	.3
	.2	.2	.2	.2	.2	.2	.2	.2	.2	.2	.2	.2	.2	.2	.2	.2	.2	.2	.2	.2
	.1	.1	.1	.1	.1	.1	.1	.1	.1	.1	.1	.1	.1	.1	.1	.1	.1	.1	.1	.1
	.0	.0	.0	.0	.0	.0	.0	.0	.0	.0	.0	.0	.0	.0	.0	.0	.0	.0	.0	.0

Luteal Phase: ________ **Ovulation:** __________

21	22	23	24	25	26	27	28	29	30	31	32	33	34	35

21	22	23	24	25	26	27	28	29	30	31	32	33	34	35
.8	.8	.8	.8	.8	.8	.8	.8	.8	.8	.8	.8	.8	.8	.8
.7	.7	.7	.7	.7	.7	.7	.7	.7	.7	.7	.7	.7	.7	.7
.6	.6	.6	.6	.6	.6	.6	.6	.6	.6	.6	.6	.6	.6	.6
.5	.5	.5	.5	.5	.5	.5	.5	.5	.5	.5	.5	.5	.5	.5
.4	.4	.4	.4	.4	.4	.4	.4	.4	.4	.4	.4	.4	.4	.4
.3	.3	.3	.3	.3	.3	.3	.3	.3	.3	.3	.3	.3	.3	.3
.2	.2	.2	.2	.2	.2	.2	.2	.2	.2	.2	.2	.2	.2	.2
.1	.1	.1	.1	.1	.1	.1	.1	.1	.1	.1	.1	.1	.1	.1
.0	.0	.0	.0	.0	.0	.0	.0	.0	.0	.0	.0	.0	.0	.0
.9	.9	.9	.9	.9	.9	.9	.9	.9	.9	.9	.9	.9	.9	.9
.8	.8	.8	.8	.8	.8	.8	.8	.8	.8	.8	.8	.8	.8	.8
.7	.7	.7	.7	.7	.7	.7	.7	.7	.7	.7	.7	.7	.7	.7
.6	.6	.6	.6	.6	.6	.6	.6	.6	.6	.6	.6	.6	.6	.6
.5	.5	.5	.5	.5	.5	.5	.5	.5	.5	.5	.5	.5	.5	.5
.4	.4	.4	.4	.4	.4	.4	.4	.4	.4	.4	.4	.4	.4	.4
.3	.3	.3	.3	.3	.3	.3	.3	.3	.3	.3	.3	.3	.3	.3
.2	.2	.2	.2	.2	.2	.2	.2	.2	.2	.2	.2	.2	.2	.2
.1	.1	.1	.1	.1	.1	.1	.1	.1	.1	.1	.1	.1	.1	.1
.0	.0	.0	.0	.0	.0	.0	.0	.0	.0	.0	.0	.0	.0	.0

Daily Notes

1 ____
2 ____
3 ____
4 ____
5 ____
6 ____
7 ____
8 ____
9 ____
10 ____
11 ____
12 ____
13 ____
14 ____
15 ____
16 ____
17 ____
18 ____
19 ____
20 ____
21 ____
22 ____
23 ____
24 ____
25 ____
26 ____
27 ____
28 ____
29 ____
30 ____
31 ____
32 ____
33 ____
34 ____
35 ____

Cycle: ___ Month(s): __________ Year: _____ Length: _______

Cycle Day	1	2	3	4	5	6	7	8	9	10	11	12	13	14	15	16	17	18	19	20
Weekday																				
Date																				
Mucus Pattern																				
Sensation																				
Mucus Description																				
Sex																				
Cervical Position																				

Cycle Day	1	2	3	4	5	6	7	8	9	10	11	12	13	14	15	16	17	18	19	20
Time																				
Luteal Phase Count																				
Temperature	.8	.8	.8	.8	.8	.8	.8	.8	.8	.8	.8	.8	.8	.8	.8	.8	.8	.8	.8	.8
	.7	.7	.7	.7	.7	.7	.7	.7	.7	.7	.7	.7	.7	.7	.7	.7	.7	.7	.7	.7
	.6	.6	.6	.6	.6	.6	.6	.6	.6	.6	.6	.6	.6	.6	.6	.6	.6	.6	.6	.6
	.5	.5	.5	.5	.5	.5	.5	.5	.5	.5	.5	.5	.5	.5	.5	.5	.5	.5	.5	.5
98°	.4	.4	.4	.4	.4	.4	.4	.4	.4	.4	.4	.4	.4	.4	.4	.4	.4	.4	.4	.4
	.3	.3	.3	.3	.3	.3	.3	.3	.3	.3	.3	.3	.3	.3	.3	.3	.3	.3	.3	.3
	.2	.2	.2	.2	.2	.2	.2	.2	.2	.2	.2	.2	.2	.2	.2	.2	.2	.2	.2	.2
	.1	.1	.1	.1	.1	.1	.1	.1	.1	.1	.1	.1	.1	.1	.1	.1	.1	.1	.1	.1
	.0	.0	.0	.0	.0	.0	.0	.0	.0	.0	.0	.0	.0	.0	.0	.0	.0	.0	.0	.0
	.9	.9	.9	.9	.9	.9	.9	.9	.9	.9	.9	.9	.9	.9	.9	.9	.9	.9	.9	.9
	.8	.8	.8	.8	.8	.8	.8	.8	.8	.8	.8	.8	.8	.8	.8	.8	.8	.8	.8	.8
	.7	.7	.7	.7	.7	.7	.7	.7	.7	.7	.7	.7	.7	.7	.7	.7	.7	.7	.7	.7
	.6	.6	.6	.6	.6	.6	.6	.6	.6	.6	.6	.6	.6	.6	.6	.6	.6	.6	.6	.6
97°	.5	.5	.5	.5	.5	.5	.5	.5	.5	.5	.5	.5	.5	.5	.5	.5	.5	.5	.5	.5
	.4	.4	.4	.4	.4	.4	.4	.4	.4	.4	.4	.4	.4	.4	.4	.4	.4	.4	.4	.4
	.3	.3	.3	.3	.3	.3	.3	.3	.3	.3	.3	.3	.3	.3	.3	.3	.3	.3	.3	.3
	.2	.2	.2	.2	.2	.2	.2	.2	.2	.2	.2	.2	.2	.2	.2	.2	.2	.2	.2	.2
	.1	.1	.1	.1	.1	.1	.1	.1	.1	.1	.1	.1	.1	.1	.1	.1	.1	.1	.1	.1
	.0	.0	.0	.0	.0	.0	.0	.0	.0	.0	.0	.0	.0	.0	.0	.0	.0	.0	.0	.0

Luteal Phase: ________ **Ovulation:** __________

21	22	23	24	25	26	27	28	29	30	31	32	33	34	35

21	22	23	24	25	26	27	28	29	30	31	32	33	34	35
.8	.8	.8	.8	.8	.8	.8	.8	.8	.8	.8	.8	.8	.8	.8
.7	.7	.7	.7	.7	.7	.7	.7	.7	.7	.7	.7	.7	.7	.7
.6	.6	.6	.6	.6	.6	.6	.6	.6	.6	.6	.6	.6	.6	.6
.5	.5	.5	.5	.5	.5	.5	.5	.5	.5	.5	.5	.5	.5	.5
.4	.4	.4	.4	.4	.4	.4	.4	.4	.4	.4	.4	.4	.4	.4
.3	.3	.3	.3	.3	.3	.3	.3	.3	.3	.3	.3	.3	.3	.3
.2	.2	.2	.2	.2	.2	.2	.2	.2	.2	.2	.2	.2	.2	.2
.1	.1	.1	.1	.1	.1	.1	.1	.1	.1	.1	.1	.1	.1	.1
.0	.0	.0	.0	.0	.0	.0	.0	.0	.0	.0	.0	.0	.0	.0
.9	.9	.9	.9	.9	.9	.9	.9	.9	.9	.9	.9	.9	.9	.9
.8	.8	.8	.8	.8	.8	.8	.8	.8	.8	.8	.8	.8	.8	.8
.7	.7	.7	.7	.7	.7	.7	.7	.7	.7	.7	.7	.7	.7	.7
.6	.6	.6	.6	.6	.6	.6	.6	.6	.6	.6	.6	.6	.6	.6
.5	.5	.5	.5	.5	.5	.5	.5	.5	.5	.5	.5	.5	.5	.5
.4	.4	.4	.4	.4	.4	.4	.4	.4	.4	.4	.4	.4	.4	.4
.3	.3	.3	.3	.3	.3	.3	.3	.3	.3	.3	.3	.3	.3	.3
.2	.2	.2	.2	.2	.2	.2	.2	.2	.2	.2	.2	.2	.2	.2
.1	.1	.1	.1	.1	.1	.1	.1	.1	.1	.1	.1	.1	.1	.1
.0	.0	.0	.0	.0	.0	.0	.0	.0	.0	.0	.0	.0	.0	.0

Daily Notes

1 ______
2 ______
3 ______
4 ______
5 ______
6 ______
7 ______
8 ______
9 ______
10 ______
11 ______
12 ______
13 ______
14 ______
15 ______
16 ______
17 ______
18 ______
19 ______
20 ______
21 ______
22 ______
23 ______
24 ______
25 ______
26 ______
27 ______
28 ______
29 ______
30 ______
31 ______
32 ______
33 ______
34 ______
35 ______

Cycle: ___ Month(s): __________ Year: _____ Length: ________

Cycle Day	1	2	3	4	5	6	7	8	9	10	11	12	13	14	15	16	17	18	19	20
Weekday																				
Date																				
Mucus Pattern																				
Sensation																				
Mucus Description																				
Sex																				
Cervical Position																				

Cycle Day	1	2	3	4	5	6	7	8	9	10	11	12	13	14	15	16	17	18	19	20
Time																				
Luteal Phase Count																				
Temperature	.8	.8	.8	.8	.8	.8	.8	.8	.8	.8	.8	.8	.8	.8	.8	.8	.8	.8	.8	.8
	.7	.7	.7	.7	.7	.7	.7	.7	.7	.7	.7	.7	.7	.7	.7	.7	.7	.7	.7	.7
	.6	.6	.6	.6	.6	.6	.6	.6	.6	.6	.6	.6	.6	.6	.6	.6	.6	.6	.6	.6
	.5	.5	.5	.5	.5	.5	.5	.5	.5	.5	.5	.5	.5	.5	.5	.5	.5	.5	.5	.5
98°	.4	.4	.4	.4	.4	.4	.4	.4	.4	.4	.4	.4	.4	.4	.4	.4	.4	.4	.4	.4
	.3	.3	.3	.3	.3	.3	.3	.3	.3	.3	.3	.3	.3	.3	.3	.3	.3	.3	.3	.3
	.2	.2	.2	.2	.2	.2	.2	.2	.2	.2	.2	.2	.2	.2	.2	.2	.2	.2	.2	.2
	.1	.1	.1	.1	.1	.1	.1	.1	.1	.1	.1	.1	.1	.1	.1	.1	.1	.1	.1	.1
	.0	.0	.0	.0	.0	.0	.0	.0	.0	.0	.0	.0	.0	.0	.0	.0	.0	.0	.0	.0
	.9	.9	.9	.9	.9	.9	.9	.9	.9	.9	.9	.9	.9	.9	.9	.9	.9	.9	.9	.9
	.8	.8	.8	.8	.8	.8	.8	.8	.8	.8	.8	.8	.8	.8	.8	.8	.8	.8	.8	.8
	.7	.7	.7	.7	.7	.7	.7	.7	.7	.7	.7	.7	.7	.7	.7	.7	.7	.7	.7	.7
	.6	.6	.6	.6	.6	.6	.6	.6	.6	.6	.6	.6	.6	.6	.6	.6	.6	.6	.6	.6
97°	.5	.5	.5	.5	.5	.5	.5	.5	.5	.5	.5	.5	.5	.5	.5	.5	.5	.5	.5	.5
	.4	.4	.4	.4	.4	.4	.4	.4	.4	.4	.4	.4	.4	.4	.4	.4	.4	.4	.4	.4
	.3	.3	.3	.3	.3	.3	.3	.3	.3	.3	.3	.3	.3	.3	.3	.3	.3	.3	.3	.3
	.2	.2	.2	.2	.2	.2	.2	.2	.2	.2	.2	.2	.2	.2	.2	.2	.2	.2	.2	.2
	.1	.1	.1	.1	.1	.1	.1	.1	.1	.1	.1	.1	.1	.1	.1	.1	.1	.1	.1	.1
	.0	.0	.0	.0	.0	.0	.0	.0	.0	.0	.0	.0	.0	.0	.0	.0	.0	.0	.0	.0

Luteal Phase: ________ **Ovulation:** __________

21	22	23	24	25	26	27	28	29	30	31	32	33	34	35

21	22	23	24	25	26	27	28	29	30	31	32	33	34	35
.8	.8	.8	.8	.8	.8	.8	.8	.8	.8	.8	.8	.8	.8	.8
.7	.7	.7	.7	.7	.7	.7	.7	.7	.7	.7	.7	.7	.7	.7
.6	.6	.6	.6	.6	.6	.6	.6	.6	.6	.6	.6	.6	.6	.6
.5	.5	.5	.5	.5	.5	.5	.5	.5	.5	.5	.5	.5	.5	.5
.4	.4	.4	.4	.4	.4	.4	.4	.4	.4	.4	.4	.4	.4	.4
.3	.3	.3	.3	.3	.3	.3	.3	.3	.3	.3	.3	.3	.3	.3
.2	.2	.2	.2	.2	.2	.2	.2	.2	.2	.2	.2	.2	.2	.2
.1	.1	.1	.1	.1	.1	.1	.1	.1	.1	.1	.1	.1	.1	.1
.0	.0	.0	.0	.0	.0	.0	.0	.0	.0	.0	.0	.0	.0	.0
.9	.9	.9	.9	.9	.9	.9	.9	.9	.9	.9	.9	.9	.9	.9
.8	.8	.8	.8	.8	.8	.8	.8	.8	.8	.8	.8	.8	.8	.8
.7	.7	.7	.7	.7	.7	.7	.7	.7	.7	.7	.7	.7	.7	.7
.6	.6	.6	.6	.6	.6	.6	.6	.6	.6	.6	.6	.6	.6	.6
.5	.5	.5	.5	.5	.5	.5	.5	.5	.5	.5	.5	.5	.5	.5
.4	.4	.4	.4	.4	.4	.4	.4	.4	.4	.4	.4	.4	.4	.4
.3	.3	.3	.3	.3	.3	.3	.3	.3	.3	.3	.3	.3	.3	.3
.2	.2	.2	.2	.2	.2	.2	.2	.2	.2	.2	.2	.2	.2	.2
.1	.1	.1	.1	.1	.1	.1	.1	.1	.1	.1	.1	.1	.1	.1
.0	.0	.0	.0	.0	.0	.0	.0	.0	.0	.0	.0	.0	.0	.0

Daily Notes

1 ____________
2 ____________
3 ____________
4 ____________
5 ____________
6 ____________
7 ____________
8 ____________
9 ____________
10 ____________
11 ____________
12 ____________
13 ____________
14 ____________
15 ____________
16 ____________
17 ____________
18 ____________
19 ____________
20 ____________
21 ____________
22 ____________
23 ____________
24 ____________
25 ____________
26 ____________
27 ____________
28 ____________
29 ____________
30 ____________
31 ____________
32 ____________
33 ____________
34 ____________
35 ____________

Cycle: ___ Month(s): ___________ Year: _____ Length: ________

Cycle Day	1	2	3	4	5	6	7	8	9	10	11	12	13	14	15	16	17	18	19	20
Weekday																				
Date																				
Mucus Pattern																				
Sensation																				
Mucus Description																				
Sex																				
Cervical Position																				

Cycle Day	1	2	3	4	5	6	7	8	9	10	11	12	13	14	15	16	17	18	19	20
Time																				
Luteal Phase Count																				
Temperature	.8	.8	.8	.8	.8	.8	.8	.8	.8	.8	.8	.8	.8	.8	.8	.8	.8	.8	.8	.8
	.7	.7	.7	.7	.7	.7	.7	.7	.7	.7	.7	.7	.7	.7	.7	.7	.7	.7	.7	.7
	.6	.6	.6	.6	.6	.6	.6	.6	.6	.6	.6	.6	.6	.6	.6	.6	.6	.6	.6	.6
	.5	.5	.5	.5	.5	.5	.5	.5	.5	.5	.5	.5	.5	.5	.5	.5	.5	.5	.5	.5
98°	.4	.4	.4	.4	.4	.4	.4	.4	.4	.4	.4	.4	.4	.4	.4	.4	.4	.4	.4	.4
	.3	.3	.3	.3	.3	.3	.3	.3	.3	.3	.3	.3	.3	.3	.3	.3	.3	.3	.3	.3
	.2	.2	.2	.2	.2	.2	.2	.2	.2	.2	.2	.2	.2	.2	.2	.2	.2	.2	.2	.2
	.1	.1	.1	.1	.1	.1	.1	.1	.1	.1	.1	.1	.1	.1	.1	.1	.1	.1	.1	.1
	.0	.0	.0	.0	.0	.0	.0	.0	.0	.0	.0	.0	.0	.0	.0	.0	.0	.0	.0	.0
	.9	.9	.9	.9	.9	.9	.9	.9	.9	.9	.9	.9	.9	.9	.9	.9	.9	.9	.9	.9
	.8	.8	.8	.8	.8	.8	.8	.8	.8	.8	.8	.8	.8	.8	.8	.8	.8	.8	.8	.8
	.7	.7	.7	.7	.7	.7	.7	.7	.7	.7	.7	.7	.7	.7	.7	.7	.7	.7	.7	.7
	.6	.6	.6	.6	.6	.6	.6	.6	.6	.6	.6	.6	.6	.6	.6	.6	.6	.6	.6	.6
97°	.5	.5	.5	.5	.5	.5	.5	.5	.5	.5	.5	.5	.5	.5	.5	.5	.5	.5	.5	.5
	.4	.4	.4	.4	.4	.4	.4	.4	.4	.4	.4	.4	.4	.4	.4	.4	.4	.4	.4	.4
	.3	.3	.3	.3	.3	.3	.3	.3	.3	.3	.3	.3	.3	.3	.3	.3	.3	.3	.3	.3
	.2	.2	.2	.2	.2	.2	.2	.2	.2	.2	.2	.2	.2	.2	.2	.2	.2	.2	.2	.2
	.1	.1	.1	.1	.1	.1	.1	.1	.1	.1	.1	.1	.1	.1	.1	.1	.1	.1	.1	.1
	.0	.0	.0	.0	.0	.0	.0	.0	.0	.0	.0	.0	.0	.0	.0	.0	.0	.0	.0	.0

Luteal Phase: ________ **Ovulation:** __________

21 22 23 24 25 26 27 28 29 30 31 32 33 34 35

21 22 23 24 25 26 27 28 29 30 31 32 33 34 35

21	22	23	24	25	26	27	28	29	30	31	32	33	34	35
.8	.8	.8	.8	.8	.8	.8	.8	.8	.8	.8	.8	.8	.8	.8
.7	.7	.7	.7	.7	.7	.7	.7	.7	.7	.7	.7	.7	.7	.7
.6	.6	.6	.6	.6	.6	.6	.6	.6	.6	.6	.6	.6	.6	.6
.5	.5	.5	.5	.5	.5	.5	.5	.5	.5	.5	.5	.5	.5	.5
.4	.4	.4	.4	.4	.4	.4	.4	.4	.4	.4	.4	.4	.4	.4
.3	.3	.3	.3	.3	.3	.3	.3	.3	.3	.3	.3	.3	.3	.3
.2	.2	.2	.2	.2	.2	.2	.2	.2	.2	.2	.2	.2	.2	.2
.1	.1	.1	.1	.1	.1	.1	.1	.1	.1	.1	.1	.1	.1	.1
.0	.0	.0	.0	.0	.0	.0	.0	.0	.0	.0	.0	.0	.0	.0
.9	.9	.9	.9	.9	.9	.9	.9	.9	.9	.9	.9	.9	.9	.9
.8	.8	.8	.8	.8	.8	.8	.8	.8	.8	.8	.8	.8	.8	.8
.7	.7	.7	.7	.7	.7	.7	.7	.7	.7	.7	.7	.7	.7	.7
.6	.6	.6	.6	.6	.6	.6	.6	.6	.6	.6	.6	.6	.6	.6
.5	.5	.5	.5	.5	.5	.5	.5	.5	.5	.5	.5	.5	.5	.5
.4	.4	.4	.4	.4	.4	.4	.4	.4	.4	.4	.4	.4	.4	.4
.3	.3	.3	.3	.3	.3	.3	.3	.3	.3	.3	.3	.3	.3	.3
.2	.2	.2	.2	.2	.2	.2	.2	.2	.2	.2	.2	.2	.2	.2
.1	.1	.1	.1	.1	.1	.1	.1	.1	.1	.1	.1	.1	.1	.1
.0	.0	.0	.0	.0	.0	.0	.0	.0	.0	.0	.0	.0	.0	.0

Daily Notes

1 ____
2 ____
3 ____
4 ____
5 ____
6 ____
7 ____
8 ____
9 ____
10 ____
11 ____
12 ____
13 ____
14 ____
15 ____
16 ____
17 ____
18 ____
19 ____
20 ____
21 ____
22 ____
23 ____
24 ____
25 ____
26 ____
27 ____
28 ____
29 ____
30 ____
31 ____
32 ____
33 ____
34 ____
35 ____

Cycle: ___ Month(s): ___________ Year: _____ Length: ________

Cycle Day	1	2	3	4	5	6	7	8	9	10	11	12	13	14	15	16	17	18	19	20
Weekday																				
Date																				
Mucus Pattern																				
Sensation																				
Mucus Description																				
Sex																				
Cervical Position																				

Cycle Day	1	2	3	4	5	6	7	8	9	10	11	12	13	14	15	16	17	18	19	20
Time																				
Luteal Phase Count																				
Temperature	.8	.8	.8	.8	.8	.8	.8	.8	.8	.8	.8	.8	.8	.8	.8	.8	.8	.8	.8	.8
	.7	.7	.7	.7	.7	.7	.7	.7	.7	.7	.7	.7	.7	.7	.7	.7	.7	.7	.7	.7
	.6	.6	.6	.6	.6	.6	.6	.6	.6	.6	.6	.6	.6	.6	.6	.6	.6	.6	.6	.6
	.5	.5	.5	.5	.5	.5	.5	.5	.5	.5	.5	.5	.5	.5	.5	.5	.5	.5	.5	.5
98°	.4	.4	.4	.4	.4	.4	.4	.4	.4	.4	.4	.4	.4	.4	.4	.4	.4	.4	.4	.4
	.3	.3	.3	.3	.3	.3	.3	.3	.3	.3	.3	.3	.3	.3	.3	.3	.3	.3	.3	.3
	.2	.2	.2	.2	.2	.2	.2	.2	.2	.2	.2	.2	.2	.2	.2	.2	.2	.2	.2	.2
	.1	.1	.1	.1	.1	.1	.1	.1	.1	.1	.1	.1	.1	.1	.1	.1	.1	.1	.1	.1
	.0	.0	.0	.0	.0	.0	.0	.0	.0	.0	.0	.0	.0	.0	.0	.0	.0	.0	.0	.0
	.9	.9	.9	.9	.9	.9	.9	.9	.9	.9	.9	.9	.9	.9	.9	.9	.9	.9	.9	.9
	.8	.8	.8	.8	.8	.8	.8	.8	.8	.8	.8	.8	.8	.8	.8	.8	.8	.8	.8	.8
	.7	.7	.7	.7	.7	.7	.7	.7	.7	.7	.7	.7	.7	.7	.7	.7	.7	.7	.7	.7
	.6	.6	.6	.6	.6	.6	.6	.6	.6	.6	.6	.6	.6	.6	.6	.6	.6	.6	.6	.6
97°	.5	.5	.5	.5	.5	.5	.5	.5	.5	.5	.5	.5	.5	.5	.5	.5	.5	.5	.5	.5
	.4	.4	.4	.4	.4	.4	.4	.4	.4	.4	.4	.4	.4	.4	.4	.4	.4	.4	.4	.4
	.3	.3	.3	.3	.3	.3	.3	.3	.3	.3	.3	.3	.3	.3	.3	.3	.3	.3	.3	.3
	.2	.2	.2	.2	.2	.2	.2	.2	.2	.2	.2	.2	.2	.2	.2	.2	.2	.2	.2	.2
	.1	.1	.1	.1	.1	.1	.1	.1	.1	.1	.1	.1	.1	.1	.1	.1	.1	.1	.1	.1
	.0	.0	.0	.0	.0	.0	.0	.0	.0	.0	.0	.0	.0	.0	.0	.0	.0	.0	.0	.0

Luteal Phase: ________ **Ovulation:** __________

21	22	23	24	25	26	27	28	29	30	31	32	33	34	35
.8	.8	.8	.8	.8	.8	.8	.8	.8	.8	.8	.8	.8	.8	.8
.7	.7	.7	.7	.7	.7	.7	.7	.7	.7	.7	.7	.7	.7	.7
.6	.6	.6	.6	.6	.6	.6	.6	.6	.6	.6	.6	.6	.6	.6
.5	.5	.5	.5	.5	.5	.5	.5	.5	.5	.5	.5	.5	.5	.5
.4	.4	.4	.4	.4	.4	.4	.4	.4	.4	.4	.4	.4	.4	.4
.3	.3	.3	.3	.3	.3	.3	.3	.3	.3	.3	.3	.3	.3	.3
.2	.2	.2	.2	.2	.2	.2	.2	.2	.2	.2	.2	.2	.2	.2
.1	.1	.1	.1	.1	.1	.1	.1	.1	.1	.1	.1	.1	.1	.1
.0	.0	.0	.0	.0	.0	.0	.0	.0	.0	.0	.0	.0	.0	.0
.9	.9	.9	.9	.9	.9	.9	.9	.9	.9	.9	.9	.9	.9	.9
.8	.8	.8	.8	.8	.8	.8	.8	.8	.8	.8	.8	.8	.8	.8
.7	.7	.7	.7	.7	.7	.7	.7	.7	.7	.7	.7	.7	.7	.7
.6	.6	.6	.6	.6	.6	.6	.6	.6	.6	.6	.6	.6	.6	.6
.5	.5	.5	.5	.5	.5	.5	.5	.5	.5	.5	.5	.5	.5	.5
.4	.4	.4	.4	.4	.4	.4	.4	.4	.4	.4	.4	.4	.4	.4
.3	.3	.3	.3	.3	.3	.3	.3	.3	.3	.3	.3	.3	.3	.3
.2	.2	.2	.2	.2	.2	.2	.2	.2	.2	.2	.2	.2	.2	.2
.1	.1	.1	.1	.1	.1	.1	.1	.1	.1	.1	.1	.1	.1	.1
.0	.0	.0	.0	.0	.0	.0	.0	.0	.0	.0	.0	.0	.0	.0

Daily Notes

1 ____
2 ____
3 ____
4 ____
5 ____
6 ____
7 ____
8 ____
9 ____
10 ____
11 ____
12 ____
13 ____
14 ____
15 ____
16 ____
17 ____
18 ____
19 ____
20 ____
21 ____
22 ____
23 ____
24 ____
25 ____
26 ____
27 ____
28 ____
29 ____
30 ____
31 ____
32 ____
33 ____
34 ____
35 ____

Cycle: ____ **Month(s):** ____________ **Year:** ______ **Length:** _________

Cycle Day	1	2	3	4	5	6	7	8	9	10	11	12	13	14	15	16	17	18	19	20
Weekday																				
Date																				
Mucus Pattern																				
Sensation																				
Mucus Description																				
Sex																				
Cervical Position																				

Cycle Day	1	2	3	4	5	6	7	8	9	10	11	12	13	14	15	16	17	18	19	20
Time																				
Luteal Phase Count																				
Temperature	.8	.8	.8	.8	.8	.8	.8	.8	.8	.8	.8	.8	.8	.8	.8	.8	.8	.8	.8	.8
	.7	.7	.7	.7	.7	.7	.7	.7	.7	.7	.7	.7	.7	.7	.7	.7	.7	.7	.7	.7
	.6	.6	.6	.6	.6	.6	.6	.6	.6	.6	.6	.6	.6	.6	.6	.6	.6	.6	.6	.6
	.5	.5	.5	.5	.5	.5	.5	.5	.5	.5	.5	.5	.5	.5	.5	.5	.5	.5	.5	.5
98°	.4	.4	.4	.4	.4	.4	.4	.4	.4	.4	.4	.4	.4	.4	.4	.4	.4	.4	.4	.4
	.3	.3	.3	.3	.3	.3	.3	.3	.3	.3	.3	.3	.3	.3	.3	.3	.3	.3	.3	.3
	.2	.2	.2	.2	.2	.2	.2	.2	.2	.2	.2	.2	.2	.2	.2	.2	.2	.2	.2	.2
	.1	.1	.1	.1	.1	.1	.1	.1	.1	.1	.1	.1	.1	.1	.1	.1	.1	.1	.1	.1
	.0	.0	.0	.0	.0	.0	.0	.0	.0	.0	.0	.0	.0	.0	.0	.0	.0	.0	.0	.0
	.9	.9	.9	.9	.9	.9	.9	.9	.9	.9	.9	.9	.9	.9	.9	.9	.9	.9	.9	.9
	.8	.8	.8	.8	.8	.8	.8	.8	.8	.8	.8	.8	.8	.8	.8	.8	.8	.8	.8	.8
	.7	.7	.7	.7	.7	.7	.7	.7	.7	.7	.7	.7	.7	.7	.7	.7	.7	.7	.7	.7
	.6	.6	.6	.6	.6	.6	.6	.6	.6	.6	.6	.6	.6	.6	.6	.6	.6	.6	.6	.6
97°	.5	.5	.5	.5	.5	.5	.5	.5	.5	.5	.5	.5	.5	.5	.5	.5	.5	.5	.5	.5
	.4	.4	.4	.4	.4	.4	.4	.4	.4	.4	.4	.4	.4	.4	.4	.4	.4	.4	.4	.4
	.3	.3	.3	.3	.3	.3	.3	.3	.3	.3	.3	.3	.3	.3	.3	.3	.3	.3	.3	.3
	.2	.2	.2	.2	.2	.2	.2	.2	.2	.2	.2	.2	.2	.2	.2	.2	.2	.2	.2	.2
	.1	.1	.1	.1	.1	.1	.1	.1	.1	.1	.1	.1	.1	.1	.1	.1	.1	.1	.1	.1
	.0	.0	.0	.0	.0	.0	.0	.0	.0	.0	.0	.0	.0	.0	.0	.0	.0	.0	.0	.0

Luteal Phase: ________ **Ovulation:** __________

21	22	23	24	25	26	27	28	29	30	31	32	33	34	35

21	22	23	24	25	26	27	28	29	30	31	32	33	34	35
.8	.8	.8	.8	.8	.8	.8	.8	.8	.8	.8	.8	.8	.8	.8
.7	.7	.7	.7	.7	.7	.7	.7	.7	.7	.7	.7	.7	.7	.7
.6	.6	.6	.6	.6	.6	.6	.6	.6	.6	.6	.6	.6	.6	.6
.5	.5	.5	.5	.5	.5	.5	.5	.5	.5	.5	.5	.5	.5	.5
.4	.4	.4	.4	.4	.4	.4	.4	.4	.4	.4	.4	.4	.4	.4
.3	.3	.3	.3	.3	.3	.3	.3	.3	.3	.3	.3	.3	.3	.3
.2	.2	.2	.2	.2	.2	.2	.2	.2	.2	.2	.2	.2	.2	.2
.1	.1	.1	.1	.1	.1	.1	.1	.1	.1	.1	.1	.1	.1	.1
.0	.0	.0	.0	.0	.0	.0	.0	.0	.0	.0	.0	.0	.0	.0
.9	.9	.9	.9	.9	.9	.9	.9	.9	.9	.9	.9	.9	.9	.9
.8	.8	.8	.8	.8	.8	.8	.8	.8	.8	.8	.8	.8	.8	.8
.7	.7	.7	.7	.7	.7	.7	.7	.7	.7	.7	.7	.7	.7	.7
.6	.6	.6	.6	.6	.6	.6	.6	.6	.6	.6	.6	.6	.6	.6
.5	.5	.5	.5	.5	.5	.5	.5	.5	.5	.5	.5	.5	.5	.5
.4	.4	.4	.4	.4	.4	.4	.4	.4	.4	.4	.4	.4	.4	.4
.3	.3	.3	.3	.3	.3	.3	.3	.3	.3	.3	.3	.3	.3	.3
.2	.2	.2	.2	.2	.2	.2	.2	.2	.2	.2	.2	.2	.2	.2
.1	.1	.1	.1	.1	.1	.1	.1	.1	.1	.1	.1	.1	.1	.1
.0	.0	.0	.0	.0	.0	.0	.0	.0	.0	.0	.0	.0	.0	.0

Daily Notes

1 ____________________

2 ____________________

3 ____________________

4 ____________________

5 ____________________

6 ____________________

7 ____________________

8 ____________________

9 ____________________

10 ____________________

11 ____________________

12 ____________________

13 ____________________

14 ____________________

15 ____________________

16 ____________________

17 ____________________

18 ____________________

19 ____________________

20 ____________________

21 ____________________

22 ____________________

23 ____________________

24 ____________________

25 ____________________

26 ____________________

27 ____________________

28 ____________________

29 ____________________

30 ____________________

31 ____________________

32 ____________________

33 ____________________

34 ____________________

35 ____________________

Cycle: ___ Month(s): __________ Year: _____ Length: _______

Cycle Day	1	2	3	4	5	6	7	8	9	10	11	12	13	14	15	16	17	18	19	20
Weekday																				
Date																				
Mucus Pattern																				
Sensation																				
Mucus Description																				
Sex	○	○	○	○	○	○	○	○	○	○	○	○	○	○	○	○	○	○	○	○
Cervical Position																				
	○	○	○	○	○	○	○	○	○	○	○	○	○	○	○	○	○	○	○	○

Cycle Day	1	2	3	4	5	6	7	8	9	10	11	12	13	14	15	16	17	18	19	20
Time																				
Luteal Phase Count																				
Temperature	.8	.8	.8	.8	.8	.8	.8	.8	.8	.8	.8	.8	.8	.8	.8	.8	.8	.8	.8	.8
	.7	.7	.7	.7	.7	.7	.7	.7	.7	.7	.7	.7	.7	.7	.7	.7	.7	.7	.7	.7
	.6	.6	.6	.6	.6	.6	.6	.6	.6	.6	.6	.6	.6	.6	.6	.6	.6	.6	.6	.6
	.5	.5	.5	.5	.5	.5	.5	.5	.5	.5	.5	.5	.5	.5	.5	.5	.5	.5	.5	.5
98°	.4	.4	.4	.4	.4	.4	.4	.4	.4	.4	.4	.4	.4	.4	.4	.4	.4	.4	.4	.4
	.3	.3	.3	.3	.3	.3	.3	.3	.3	.3	.3	.3	.3	.3	.3	.3	.3	.3	.3	.3
	.2	.2	.2	.2	.2	.2	.2	.2	.2	.2	.2	.2	.2	.2	.2	.2	.2	.2	.2	.2
	.1	.1	.1	.1	.1	.1	.1	.1	.1	.1	.1	.1	.1	.1	.1	.1	.1	.1	.1	.1
	.0	.0	.0	.0	.0	.0	.0	.0	.0	.0	.0	.0	.0	.0	.0	.0	.0	.0	.0	.0
	.9	.9	.9	.9	.9	.9	.9	.9	.9	.9	.9	.9	.9	.9	.9	.9	.9	.9	.9	.9
	.8	.8	.8	.8	.8	.8	.8	.8	.8	.8	.8	.8	.8	.8	.8	.8	.8	.8	.8	.8
	.7	.7	.7	.7	.7	.7	.7	.7	.7	.7	.7	.7	.7	.7	.7	.7	.7	.7	.7	.7
	.6	.6	.6	.6	.6	.6	.6	.6	.6	.6	.6	.6	.6	.6	.6	.6	.6	.6	.6	.6
97°	.5	.5	.5	.5	.5	.5	.5	.5	.5	.5	.5	.5	.5	.5	.5	.5	.5	.5	.5	.5
	.4	.4	.4	.4	.4	.4	.4	.4	.4	.4	.4	.4	.4	.4	.4	.4	.4	.4	.4	.4
	.3	.3	.3	.3	.3	.3	.3	.3	.3	.3	.3	.3	.3	.3	.3	.3	.3	.3	.3	.3
	.2	.2	.2	.2	.2	.2	.2	.2	.2	.2	.2	.2	.2	.2	.2	.2	.2	.2	.2	.2
	.1	.1	.1	.1	.1	.1	.1	.1	.1	.1	.1	.1	.1	.1	.1	.1	.1	.1	.1	.1
	.0	.0	.0	.0	.0	.0	.0	.0	.0	.0	.0	.0	.0	.0	.0	.0	.0	.0	.0	.0

Luteal Phase: ________ **Ovulation:** __________

21	22	23	24	25	26	27	28	29	30	31	32	33	34	35

21	22	23	24	25	26	27	28	29	30	31	32	33	34	35
.8	.8	.8	.8	.8	.8	.8	.8	.8	.8	.8	.8	.8	.8	.8
.7	.7	.7	.7	.7	.7	.7	.7	.7	.7	.7	.7	.7	.7	.7
.6	.6	.6	.6	.6	.6	.6	.6	.6	.6	.6	.6	.6	.6	.6
.5	.5	.5	.5	.5	.5	.5	.5	.5	.5	.5	.5	.5	.5	.5
.4	.4	.4	.4	.4	.4	.4	.4	.4	.4	.4	.4	.4	.4	.4
.3	.3	.3	.3	.3	.3	.3	.3	.3	.3	.3	.3	.3	.3	.3
.2	.2	.2	.2	.2	.2	.2	.2	.2	.2	.2	.2	.2	.2	.2
.1	.1	.1	.1	.1	.1	.1	.1	.1	.1	.1	.1	.1	.1	.1
.0	.0	.0	.0	.0	.0	.0	.0	.0	.0	.0	.0	.0	.0	.0
.9	.9	.9	.9	.9	.9	.9	.9	.9	.9	.9	.9	.9	.9	.9
.8	.8	.8	.8	.8	.8	.8	.8	.8	.8	.8	.8	.8	.8	.8
.7	.7	.7	.7	.7	.7	.7	.7	.7	.7	.7	.7	.7	.7	.7
.6	.6	.6	.6	.6	.6	.6	.6	.6	.6	.6	.6	.6	.6	.6
.5	.5	.5	.5	.5	.5	.5	.5	.5	.5	.5	.5	.5	.5	.5
.4	.4	.4	.4	.4	.4	.4	.4	.4	.4	.4	.4	.4	.4	.4
.3	.3	.3	.3	.3	.3	.3	.3	.3	.3	.3	.3	.3	.3	.3
.2	.2	.2	.2	.2	.2	.2	.2	.2	.2	.2	.2	.2	.2	.2
.1	.1	.1	.1	.1	.1	.1	.1	.1	.1	.1	.1	.1	.1	.1
.0	.0	.0	.0	.0	.0	.0	.0	.0	.0	.0	.0	.0	.0	.0

Daily Notes

1 ____________________
2 ____________________
3 ____________________
4 ____________________
5 ____________________
6 ____________________
7 ____________________
8 ____________________
9 ____________________
10 ____________________
11 ____________________
12 ____________________
13 ____________________
14 ____________________
15 ____________________
16 ____________________
17 ____________________
18 ____________________
19 ____________________
20 ____________________
21 ____________________
22 ____________________
23 ____________________
24 ____________________
25 ____________________
26 ____________________
27 ____________________
28 ____________________
29 ____________________
30 ____________________
31 ____________________
32 ____________________
33 ____________________
34 ____________________
35 ____________________

Cycle: ___ Month(s): ___________ Year: _____ Length: ________

Cycle Day	1	2	3	4	5	6	7	8	9	10	11	12	13	14	15	16	17	18	19	20
Weekday																				
Date																				
Mucus Pattern																				
Sensation																				
Mucus Description																				
Sex																				
Cervical Position																				

Cycle Day	1	2	3	4	5	6	7	8	9	10	11	12	13	14	15	16	17	18	19	20
Time																				
Luteal Phase Count																				
Temperature	.8	.8	.8	.8	.8	.8	.8	.8	.8	.8	.8	.8	.8	.8	.8	.8	.8	.8	.8	.8
	.7	.7	.7	.7	.7	.7	.7	.7	.7	.7	.7	.7	.7	.7	.7	.7	.7	.7	.7	.7
	.6	.6	.6	.6	.6	.6	.6	.6	.6	.6	.6	.6	.6	.6	.6	.6	.6	.6	.6	.6
	.5	.5	.5	.5	.5	.5	.5	.5	.5	.5	.5	.5	.5	.5	.5	.5	.5	.5	.5	.5
98°	.4	.4	.4	.4	.4	.4	.4	.4	.4	.4	.4	.4	.4	.4	.4	.4	.4	.4	.4	.4
	.3	.3	.3	.3	.3	.3	.3	.3	.3	.3	.3	.3	.3	.3	.3	.3	.3	.3	.3	.3
	.2	.2	.2	.2	.2	.2	.2	.2	.2	.2	.2	.2	.2	.2	.2	.2	.2	.2	.2	.2
	.1	.1	.1	.1	.1	.1	.1	.1	.1	.1	.1	.1	.1	.1	.1	.1	.1	.1	.1	.1
	.0	.0	.0	.0	.0	.0	.0	.0	.0	.0	.0	.0	.0	.0	.0	.0	.0	.0	.0	.0
	.9	.9	.9	.9	.9	.9	.9	.9	.9	.9	.9	.9	.9	.9	.9	.9	.9	.9	.9	.9
	.8	.8	.8	.8	.8	.8	.8	.8	.8	.8	.8	.8	.8	.8	.8	.8	.8	.8	.8	.8
	.7	.7	.7	.7	.7	.7	.7	.7	.7	.7	.7	.7	.7	.7	.7	.7	.7	.7	.7	.7
	.6	.6	.6	.6	.6	.6	.6	.6	.6	.6	.6	.6	.6	.6	.6	.6	.6	.6	.6	.6
97°	.5	.5	.5	.5	.5	.5	.5	.5	.5	.5	.5	.5	.5	.5	.5	.5	.5	.5	.5	.5
	.4	.4	.4	.4	.4	.4	.4	.4	.4	.4	.4	.4	.4	.4	.4	.4	.4	.4	.4	.4
	.3	.3	.3	.3	.3	.3	.3	.3	.3	.3	.3	.3	.3	.3	.3	.3	.3	.3	.3	.3
	.2	.2	.2	.2	.2	.2	.2	.2	.2	.2	.2	.2	.2	.2	.2	.2	.2	.2	.2	.2
	.1	.1	.1	.1	.1	.1	.1	.1	.1	.1	.1	.1	.1	.1	.1	.1	.1	.1	.1	.1
	.0	.0	.0	.0	.0	.0	.0	.0	.0	.0	.0	.0	.0	.0	.0	.0	.0	.0	.0	.0

Luteal Phase: ________ **Ovulation:** __________

21	22	23	24	25	26	27	28	29	30	31	32	33	34	35
.8	.8	.8	.8	.8	.8	.8	.8	.8	.8	.8	.8	.8	.8	.8
.7	.7	.7	.7	.7	.7	.7	.7	.7	.7	.7	.7	.7	.7	.7
.6	.6	.6	.6	.6	.6	.6	.6	.6	.6	.6	.6	.6	.6	.6
.5	.5	.5	.5	.5	.5	.5	.5	.5	.5	.5	.5	.5	.5	.5
.4	.4	.4	.4	.4	.4	.4	.4	.4	.4	.4	.4	.4	.4	.4
.3	.3	.3	.3	.3	.3	.3	.3	.3	.3	.3	.3	.3	.3	.3
.2	.2	.2	.2	.2	.2	.2	.2	.2	.2	.2	.2	.2	.2	.2
.1	.1	.1	.1	.1	.1	.1	.1	.1	.1	.1	.1	.1	.1	.1
.0	.0	.0	.0	.0	.0	.0	.0	.0	.0	.0	.0	.0	.0	.0
.9	.9	.9	.9	.9	.9	.9	.9	.9	.9	.9	.9	.9	.9	.9
.8	.8	.8	.8	.8	.8	.8	.8	.8	.8	.8	.8	.8	.8	.8
.7	.7	.7	.7	.7	.7	.7	.7	.7	.7	.7	.7	.7	.7	.7
.6	.6	.6	.6	.6	.6	.6	.6	.6	.6	.6	.6	.6	.6	.6
.5	.5	.5	.5	.5	.5	.5	.5	.5	.5	.5	.5	.5	.5	.5
.4	.4	.4	.4	.4	.4	.4	.4	.4	.4	.4	.4	.4	.4	.4
.3	.3	.3	.3	.3	.3	.3	.3	.3	.3	.3	.3	.3	.3	.3
.2	.2	.2	.2	.2	.2	.2	.2	.2	.2	.2	.2	.2	.2	.2
.1	.1	.1	.1	.1	.1	.1	.1	.1	.1	.1	.1	.1	.1	.1
.0	.0	.0	.0	.0	.0	.0	.0	.0	.0	.0	.0	.0	.0	.0

Daily Notes

1 ____________________
2 ____________________
3 ____________________
4 ____________________
5 ____________________
6 ____________________
7 ____________________
8 ____________________
9 ____________________
10 ____________________
11 ____________________
12 ____________________
13 ____________________
14 ____________________
15 ____________________
16 ____________________
17 ____________________
18 ____________________
19 ____________________
20 ____________________
21 ____________________
22 ____________________
23 ____________________
24 ____________________
25 ____________________
26 ____________________
27 ____________________
28 ____________________
29 ____________________
30 ____________________
31 ____________________
32 ____________________
33 ____________________
34 ____________________
35 ____________________

Cycle: ____ **Month(s):** ____________ **Year:** ______ **Length:** _________

Cycle Day	1	2	3	4	5	6	7	8	9	10	11	12	13	14	15	16	17	18	19	20
Weekday																				
Date																				
Mucus Pattern																				
Sensation																				
Mucus Description																				
Sex																				
Cervical Position																				

Cycle Day	1	2	3	4	5	6	7	8	9	10	11	12	13	14	15	16	17	18	19	20
Time																				
Luteal Phase Count																				
Temperature	.8	.8	.8	.8	.8	.8	.8	.8	.8	.8	.8	.8	.8	.8	.8	.8	.8	.8	.8	.8
	.7	.7	.7	.7	.7	.7	.7	.7	.7	.7	.7	.7	.7	.7	.7	.7	.7	.7	.7	.7
	.6	.6	.6	.6	.6	.6	.6	.6	.6	.6	.6	.6	.6	.6	.6	.6	.6	.6	.6	.6
	.5	.5	.5	.5	.5	.5	.5	.5	.5	.5	.5	.5	.5	.5	.5	.5	.5	.5	.5	.5
98°	.4	.4	.4	.4	.4	.4	.4	.4	.4	.4	.4	.4	.4	.4	.4	.4	.4	.4	.4	.4
	.3	.3	.3	.3	.3	.3	.3	.3	.3	.3	.3	.3	.3	.3	.3	.3	.3	.3	.3	.3
	.2	.2	.2	.2	.2	.2	.2	.2	.2	.2	.2	.2	.2	.2	.2	.2	.2	.2	.2	.2
	.1	.1	.1	.1	.1	.1	.1	.1	.1	.1	.1	.1	.1	.1	.1	.1	.1	.1	.1	.1
	.0	.0	.0	.0	.0	.0	.0	.0	.0	.0	.0	.0	.0	.0	.0	.0	.0	.0	.0	.0
	.9	.9	.9	.9	.9	.9	.9	.9	.9	.9	.9	.9	.9	.9	.9	.9	.9	.9	.9	.9
	.8	.8	.8	.8	.8	.8	.8	.8	.8	.8	.8	.8	.8	.8	.8	.8	.8	.8	.8	.8
	.7	.7	.7	.7	.7	.7	.7	.7	.7	.7	.7	.7	.7	.7	.7	.7	.7	.7	.7	.7
	.6	.6	.6	.6	.6	.6	.6	.6	.6	.6	.6	.6	.6	.6	.6	.6	.6	.6	.6	.6
97°	.5	.5	.5	.5	.5	.5	.5	.5	.5	.5	.5	.5	.5	.5	.5	.5	.5	.5	.5	.5
	.4	.4	.4	.4	.4	.4	.4	.4	.4	.4	.4	.4	.4	.4	.4	.4	.4	.4	.4	.4
	.3	.3	.3	.3	.3	.3	.3	.3	.3	.3	.3	.3	.3	.3	.3	.3	.3	.3	.3	.3
	.2	.2	.2	.2	.2	.2	.2	.2	.2	.2	.2	.2	.2	.2	.2	.2	.2	.2	.2	.2
	.1	.1	.1	.1	.1	.1	.1	.1	.1	.1	.1	.1	.1	.1	.1	.1	.1	.1	.1	.1
	.0	.0	.0	.0	.0	.0	.0	.0	.0	.0	.0	.0	.0	.0	.0	.0	.0	.0	.0	.0

Luteal Phase: ________ **Ovulation:** __________

21	22	23	24	25	26	27	28	29	30	31	32	33	34	35

21	22	23	24	25	26	27	28	29	30	31	32	33	34	35

.8	.8	.8	.8	.8	.8	.8	.8	.8	.8	.8	.8	.8	.8	.8
.7	.7	.7	.7	.7	.7	.7	.7	.7	.7	.7	.7	.7	.7	.7
.6	.6	.6	.6	.6	.6	.6	.6	.6	.6	.6	.6	.6	.6	.6
.5	.5	.5	.5	.5	.5	.5	.5	.5	.5	.5	.5	.5	.5	.5
.4	.4	.4	.4	.4	.4	.4	.4	.4	.4	.4	.4	.4	.4	.4
.3	.3	.3	.3	.3	.3	.3	.3	.3	.3	.3	.3	.3	.3	.3
.2	.2	.2	.2	.2	.2	.2	.2	.2	.2	.2	.2	.2	.2	.2
.1	.1	.1	.1	.1	.1	.1	.1	.1	.1	.1	.1	.1	.1	.1
.0	.0	.0	.0	.0	.0	.0	.0	.0	.0	.0	.0	.0	.0	.0
.9	.9	.9	.9	.9	.9	.9	.9	.9	.9	.9	.9	.9	.9	.9
.8	.8	.8	.8	.8	.8	.8	.8	.8	.8	.8	.8	.8	.8	.8
.7	.7	.7	.7	.7	.7	.7	.7	.7	.7	.7	.7	.7	.7	.7
.6	.6	.6	.6	.6	.6	.6	.6	.6	.6	.6	.6	.6	.6	.6
.5	.5	.5	.5	.5	.5	.5	.5	.5	.5	.5	.5	.5	.5	.5
.4	.4	.4	.4	.4	.4	.4	.4	.4	.4	.4	.4	.4	.4	.4
.3	.3	.3	.3	.3	.3	.3	.3	.3	.3	.3	.3	.3	.3	.3
.2	.2	.2	.2	.2	.2	.2	.2	.2	.2	.2	.2	.2	.2	.2
.1	.1	.1	.1	.1	.1	.1	.1	.1	.1	.1	.1	.1	.1	.1
.0	.0	.0	.0	.0	.0	.0	.0	.0	.0	.0	.0	.0	.0	.0

Daily Notes

1 ____________________
2 ____________________
3 ____________________
4 ____________________
5 ____________________
6 ____________________
7 ____________________
8 ____________________
9 ____________________
10 ____________________
11 ____________________
12 ____________________
13 ____________________
14 ____________________
15 ____________________
16 ____________________
17 ____________________
18 ____________________
19 ____________________
20 ____________________
21 ____________________
22 ____________________
23 ____________________
24 ____________________
25 ____________________
26 ____________________
27 ____________________
28 ____________________
29 ____________________
30 ____________________
31 ____________________
32 ____________________
33 ____________________
34 ____________________
35 ____________________

Cycle: ___ Month(s): ___________ Year: _____ Length: ________

Cycle Day	1	2	3	4	5	6	7	8	9	10	11	12	13	14	15	16	17	18	19	20
Weekday																				
Date																				
Mucus Pattern																				
Sensation																				
Mucus Description																				
Sex																				
Cervical Position																				

Cycle Day	1	2	3	4	5	6	7	8	9	10	11	12	13	14	15	16	17	18	19	20
Time																				
Luteal Phase Count																				
Temperature	.8	.8	.8	.8	.8	.8	.8	.8	.8	.8	.8	.8	.8	.8	.8	.8	.8	.8	.8	.8
	.7	.7	.7	.7	.7	.7	.7	.7	.7	.7	.7	.7	.7	.7	.7	.7	.7	.7	.7	.7
	.6	.6	.6	.6	.6	.6	.6	.6	.6	.6	.6	.6	.6	.6	.6	.6	.6	.6	.6	.6
	.5	.5	.5	.5	.5	.5	.5	.5	.5	.5	.5	.5	.5	.5	.5	.5	.5	.5	.5	.5
98°	.4	.4	.4	.4	.4	.4	.4	.4	.4	.4	.4	.4	.4	.4	.4	.4	.4	.4	.4	.4
	.3	.3	.3	.3	.3	.3	.3	.3	.3	.3	.3	.3	.3	.3	.3	.3	.3	.3	.3	.3
	.2	.2	.2	.2	.2	.2	.2	.2	.2	.2	.2	.2	.2	.2	.2	.2	.2	.2	.2	.2
	.1	.1	.1	.1	.1	.1	.1	.1	.1	.1	.1	.1	.1	.1	.1	.1	.1	.1	.1	.1
	.0	.0	.0	.0	.0	.0	.0	.0	.0	.0	.0	.0	.0	.0	.0	.0	.0	.0	.0	.0
	.9	.9	.9	.9	.9	.9	.9	.9	.9	.9	.9	.9	.9	.9	.9	.9	.9	.9	.9	.9
	.8	.8	.8	.8	.8	.8	.8	.8	.8	.8	.8	.8	.8	.8	.8	.8	.8	.8	.8	.8
	.7	.7	.7	.7	.7	.7	.7	.7	.7	.7	.7	.7	.7	.7	.7	.7	.7	.7	.7	.7
	.6	.6	.6	.6	.6	.6	.6	.6	.6	.6	.6	.6	.6	.6	.6	.6	.6	.6	.6	.6
97°	.5	.5	.5	.5	.5	.5	.5	.5	.5	.5	.5	.5	.5	.5	.5	.5	.5	.5	.5	.5
	.4	.4	.4	.4	.4	.4	.4	.4	.4	.4	.4	.4	.4	.4	.4	.4	.4	.4	.4	.4
	.3	.3	.3	.3	.3	.3	.3	.3	.3	.3	.3	.3	.3	.3	.3	.3	.3	.3	.3	.3
	.2	.2	.2	.2	.2	.2	.2	.2	.2	.2	.2	.2	.2	.2	.2	.2	.2	.2	.2	.2
	.1	.1	.1	.1	.1	.1	.1	.1	.1	.1	.1	.1	.1	.1	.1	.1	.1	.1	.1	.1
	.0	.0	.0	.0	.0	.0	.0	.0	.0	.0	.0	.0	.0	.0	.0	.0	.0	.0	.0	.0

Luteal Phase: ________ **Ovulation:** __________

21	22	23	24	25	26	27	28	29	30	31	32	33	34	35

21	22	23	24	25	26	27	28	29	30	31	32	33	34	35
.8	.8	.8	.8	.8	.8	.8	.8	.8	.8	.8	.8	.8	.8	.8
.7	.7	.7	.7	.7	.7	.7	.7	.7	.7	.7	.7	.7	.7	.7
.6	.6	.6	.6	.6	.6	.6	.6	.6	.6	.6	.6	.6	.6	.6
.5	.5	.5	.5	.5	.5	.5	.5	.5	.5	.5	.5	.5	.5	.5
.4	.4	.4	.4	.4	.4	.4	.4	.4	.4	.4	.4	.4	.4	.4
.3	.3	.3	.3	.3	.3	.3	.3	.3	.3	.3	.3	.3	.3	.3
.2	.2	.2	.2	.2	.2	.2	.2	.2	.2	.2	.2	.2	.2	.2
.1	.1	.1	.1	.1	.1	.1	.1	.1	.1	.1	.1	.1	.1	.1
.0	.0	.0	.0	.0	.0	.0	.0	.0	.0	.0	.0	.0	.0	.0
.9	.9	.9	.9	.9	.9	.9	.9	.9	.9	.9	.9	.9	.9	.9
.8	.8	.8	.8	.8	.8	.8	.8	.8	.8	.8	.8	.8	.8	.8
.7	.7	.7	.7	.7	.7	.7	.7	.7	.7	.7	.7	.7	.7	.7
.6	.6	.6	.6	.6	.6	.6	.6	.6	.6	.6	.6	.6	.6	.6
.5	.5	.5	.5	.5	.5	.5	.5	.5	.5	.5	.5	.5	.5	.5
.4	.4	.4	.4	.4	.4	.4	.4	.4	.4	.4	.4	.4	.4	.4
.3	.3	.3	.3	.3	.3	.3	.3	.3	.3	.3	.3	.3	.3	.3
.2	.2	.2	.2	.2	.2	.2	.2	.2	.2	.2	.2	.2	.2	.2
.1	.1	.1	.1	.1	.1	.1	.1	.1	.1	.1	.1	.1	.1	.1
.0	.0	.0	.0	.0	.0	.0	.0	.0	.0	.0	.0	.0	.0	.0

Daily Notes

1 ____________________
2 ____________________
3 ____________________
4 ____________________
5 ____________________
6 ____________________
7 ____________________
8 ____________________
9 ____________________
10 ____________________
11 ____________________
12 ____________________
13 ____________________
14 ____________________
15 ____________________
16 ____________________
17 ____________________
18 ____________________
19 ____________________
20 ____________________
21 ____________________
22 ____________________
23 ____________________
24 ____________________
25 ____________________
26 ____________________
27 ____________________
28 ____________________
29 ____________________
30 ____________________
31 ____________________
32 ____________________
33 ____________________
34 ____________________
35 ____________________

Cycle: ___ **Month(s):** ___________ **Year:** ______ **Length:** ________

Cycle Day	1	2	3	4	5	6	7	8	9	10	11	12	13	14	15	16	17	18	19	20
Weekday																				
Date																				
Mucus Pattern																				
Sensation																				
Mucus Description																				
Sex																				
Cervical Position																				

Cycle Day	1	2	3	4	5	6	7	8	9	10	11	12	13	14	15	16	17	18	19	20
Time																				
Luteal Phase Count																				
Temperature	.8	.8	.8	.8	.8	.8	.8	.8	.8	.8	.8	.8	.8	.8	.8	.8	.8	.8	.8	.8
	.7	.7	.7	.7	.7	.7	.7	.7	.7	.7	.7	.7	.7	.7	.7	.7	.7	.7	.7	.7
	.6	.6	.6	.6	.6	.6	.6	.6	.6	.6	.6	.6	.6	.6	.6	.6	.6	.6	.6	.6
	.5	.5	.5	.5	.5	.5	.5	.5	.5	.5	.5	.5	.5	.5	.5	.5	.5	.5	.5	.5
98°	.4	.4	.4	.4	.4	.4	.4	.4	.4	.4	.4	.4	.4	.4	.4	.4	.4	.4	.4	.4
	.3	.3	.3	.3	.3	.3	.3	.3	.3	.3	.3	.3	.3	.3	.3	.3	.3	.3	.3	.3
	.2	.2	.2	.2	.2	.2	.2	.2	.2	.2	.2	.2	.2	.2	.2	.2	.2	.2	.2	.2
	.1	.1	.1	.1	.1	.1	.1	.1	.1	.1	.1	.1	.1	.1	.1	.1	.1	.1	.1	.1
	.0	.0	.0	.0	.0	.0	.0	.0	.0	.0	.0	.0	.0	.0	.0	.0	.0	.0	.0	.0
	.9	.9	.9	.9	.9	.9	.9	.9	.9	.9	.9	.9	.9	.9	.9	.9	.9	.9	.9	.9
	.8	.8	.8	.8	.8	.8	.8	.8	.8	.8	.8	.8	.8	.8	.8	.8	.8	.8	.8	.8
	.7	.7	.7	.7	.7	.7	.7	.7	.7	.7	.7	.7	.7	.7	.7	.7	.7	.7	.7	.7
97°	.6	.6	.6	.6	.6	.6	.6	.6	.6	.6	.6	.6	.6	.6	.6	.6	.6	.6	.6	.6
	.5	.5	.5	.5	.5	.5	.5	.5	.5	.5	.5	.5	.5	.5	.5	.5	.5	.5	.5	.5
	.4	.4	.4	.4	.4	.4	.4	.4	.4	.4	.4	.4	.4	.4	.4	.4	.4	.4	.4	.4
	.3	.3	.3	.3	.3	.3	.3	.3	.3	.3	.3	.3	.3	.3	.3	.3	.3	.3	.3	.3
	.2	.2	.2	.2	.2	.2	.2	.2	.2	.2	.2	.2	.2	.2	.2	.2	.2	.2	.2	.2
	.1	.1	.1	.1	.1	.1	.1	.1	.1	.1	.1	.1	.1	.1	.1	.1	.1	.1	.1	.1
	.0	.0	.0	.0	.0	.0	.0	.0	.0	.0	.0	.0	.0	.0	.0	.0	.0	.0	.0	.0

Luteal Phase: ________ **Ovulation:** __________

21	22	23	24	25	26	27	28	29	30	31	32	33	34	35

21	22	23	24	25	26	27	28	29	30	31	32	33	34	35
.8	.8	.8	.8	.8	.8	.8	.8	.8	.8	.8	.8	.8	.8	.8
.7	.7	.7	.7	.7	.7	.7	.7	.7	.7	.7	.7	.7	.7	.7
.6	.6	.6	.6	.6	.6	.6	.6	.6	.6	.6	.6	.6	.6	.6
.5	.5	.5	.5	.5	.5	.5	.5	.5	.5	.5	.5	.5	.5	.5
.4	.4	.4	.4	.4	.4	.4	.4	.4	.4	.4	.4	.4	.4	.4
.3	.3	.3	.3	.3	.3	.3	.3	.3	.3	.3	.3	.3	.3	.3
.2	.2	.2	.2	.2	.2	.2	.2	.2	.2	.2	.2	.2	.2	.2
.1	.1	.1	.1	.1	.1	.1	.1	.1	.1	.1	.1	.1	.1	.1
.0	.0	.0	.0	.0	.0	.0	.0	.0	.0	.0	.0	.0	.0	.0
.9	.9	.9	.9	.9	.9	.9	.9	.9	.9	.9	.9	.9	.9	.9
.8	.8	.8	.8	.8	.8	.8	.8	.8	.8	.8	.8	.8	.8	.8
.7	.7	.7	.7	.7	.7	.7	.7	.7	.7	.7	.7	.7	.7	.7
.6	.6	.6	.6	.6	.6	.6	.6	.6	.6	.6	.6	.6	.6	.6
.5	.5	.5	.5	.5	.5	.5	.5	.5	.5	.5	.5	.5	.5	.5
.4	.4	.4	.4	.4	.4	.4	.4	.4	.4	.4	.4	.4	.4	.4
.3	.3	.3	.3	.3	.3	.3	.3	.3	.3	.3	.3	.3	.3	.3
.2	.2	.2	.2	.2	.2	.2	.2	.2	.2	.2	.2	.2	.2	.2
.1	.1	.1	.1	.1	.1	.1	.1	.1	.1	.1	.1	.1	.1	.1
.0	.0	.0	.0	.0	.0	.0	.0	.0	.0	.0	.0	.0	.0	.0

Daily Notes

1 ____________________
2 ____________________
3 ____________________
4 ____________________
5 ____________________
6 ____________________
7 ____________________
8 ____________________
9 ____________________
10 ____________________
11 ____________________
12 ____________________
13 ____________________
14 ____________________
15 ____________________
16 ____________________
17 ____________________
18 ____________________
19 ____________________
20 ____________________
21 ____________________
22 ____________________
23 ____________________
24 ____________________
25 ____________________
26 ____________________
27 ____________________
28 ____________________
29 ____________________
30 ____________________
31 ____________________
32 ____________________
33 ____________________
34 ____________________
35 ____________________

Cycle: ___ Month(s): ___________ Year: _____ Length: ________

Cycle Day	1	2	3	4	5	6	7	8	9	10	11	12	13	14	15	16	17	18	19	20
Weekday																				
Date																				
Mucus Pattern																				
Sensation																				
Mucus Description																				
Sex																				
Cervical Position																				

Cycle Day	1	2	3	4	5	6	7	8	9	10	11	12	13	14	15	16	17	18	19	20
Time																				
Luteal Phase Count																				
Temperature	.8	.8	.8	.8	.8	.8	.8	.8	.8	.8	.8	.8	.8	.8	.8	.8	.8	.8	.8	.8
	.7	.7	.7	.7	.7	.7	.7	.7	.7	.7	.7	.7	.7	.7	.7	.7	.7	.7	.7	.7
	.6	.6	.6	.6	.6	.6	.6	.6	.6	.6	.6	.6	.6	.6	.6	.6	.6	.6	.6	.6
	.5	.5	.5	.5	.5	.5	.5	.5	.5	.5	.5	.5	.5	.5	.5	.5	.5	.5	.5	.5
98°	.4	.4	.4	.4	.4	.4	.4	.4	.4	.4	.4	.4	.4	.4	.4	.4	.4	.4	.4	.4
	.3	.3	.3	.3	.3	.3	.3	.3	.3	.3	.3	.3	.3	.3	.3	.3	.3	.3	.3	.3
	.2	.2	.2	.2	.2	.2	.2	.2	.2	.2	.2	.2	.2	.2	.2	.2	.2	.2	.2	.2
	.1	.1	.1	.1	.1	.1	.1	.1	.1	.1	.1	.1	.1	.1	.1	.1	.1	.1	.1	.1
	.0	.0	.0	.0	.0	.0	.0	.0	.0	.0	.0	.0	.0	.0	.0	.0	.0	.0	.0	.0
	.9	.9	.9	.9	.9	.9	.9	.9	.9	.9	.9	.9	.9	.9	.9	.9	.9	.9	.9	.9
	.8	.8	.8	.8	.8	.8	.8	.8	.8	.8	.8	.8	.8	.8	.8	.8	.8	.8	.8	.8
	.7	.7	.7	.7	.7	.7	.7	.7	.7	.7	.7	.7	.7	.7	.7	.7	.7	.7	.7	.7
	.6	.6	.6	.6	.6	.6	.6	.6	.6	.6	.6	.6	.6	.6	.6	.6	.6	.6	.6	.6
97°	.5	.5	.5	.5	.5	.5	.5	.5	.5	.5	.5	.5	.5	.5	.5	.5	.5	.5	.5	.5
	.4	.4	.4	.4	.4	.4	.4	.4	.4	.4	.4	.4	.4	.4	.4	.4	.4	.4	.4	.4
	.3	.3	.3	.3	.3	.3	.3	.3	.3	.3	.3	.3	.3	.3	.3	.3	.3	.3	.3	.3
	.2	.2	.2	.2	.2	.2	.2	.2	.2	.2	.2	.2	.2	.2	.2	.2	.2	.2	.2	.2
	.1	.1	.1	.1	.1	.1	.1	.1	.1	.1	.1	.1	.1	.1	.1	.1	.1	.1	.1	.1
	.0	.0	.0	.0	.0	.0	.0	.0	.0	.0	.0	.0	.0	.0	.0	.0	.0	.0	.0	.0

Luteal Phase: ________ **Ovulation:** __________

21	22	23	24	25	26	27	28	29	30	31	32	33	34	35

21	22	23	24	25	26	27	28	29	30	31	32	33	34	35
.8	.8	.8	.8	.8	.8	.8	.8	.8	.8	.8	.8	.8	.8	.8
.7	.7	.7	.7	.7	.7	.7	.7	.7	.7	.7	.7	.7	.7	.7
.6	.6	.6	.6	.6	.6	.6	.6	.6	.6	.6	.6	.6	.6	.6
.5	.5	.5	.5	.5	.5	.5	.5	.5	.5	.5	.5	.5	.5	.5
.4	.4	.4	.4	.4	.4	.4	.4	.4	.4	.4	.4	.4	.4	.4
.3	.3	.3	.3	.3	.3	.3	.3	.3	.3	.3	.3	.3	.3	.3
.2	.2	.2	.2	.2	.2	.2	.2	.2	.2	.2	.2	.2	.2	.2
.1	.1	.1	.1	.1	.1	.1	.1	.1	.1	.1	.1	.1	.1	.1
.0	.0	.0	.0	.0	.0	.0	.0	.0	.0	.0	.0	.0	.0	.0
.9	.9	.9	.9	.9	.9	.9	.9	.9	.9	.9	.9	.9	.9	.9
.8	.8	.8	.8	.8	.8	.8	.8	.8	.8	.8	.8	.8	.8	.8
.7	.7	.7	.7	.7	.7	.7	.7	.7	.7	.7	.7	.7	.7	.7
.6	.6	.6	.6	.6	.6	.6	.6	.6	.6	.6	.6	.6	.6	.6
.5	.5	.5	.5	.5	.5	.5	.5	.5	.5	.5	.5	.5	.5	.5
.4	.4	.4	.4	.4	.4	.4	.4	.4	.4	.4	.4	.4	.4	.4
.3	.3	.3	.3	.3	.3	.3	.3	.3	.3	.3	.3	.3	.3	.3
.2	.2	.2	.2	.2	.2	.2	.2	.2	.2	.2	.2	.2	.2	.2
.1	.1	.1	.1	.1	.1	.1	.1	.1	.1	.1	.1	.1	.1	.1
.0	.0	.0	.0	.0	.0	.0	.0	.0	.0	.0	.0	.0	.0	.0

Daily Notes

1
2
3
4
5
6
7
8
9
10
11
12
13
14
15
16
17
18
19
20
21
22
23
24
25
26
27
28
29
30
31
32
33
34
35

Cycle: ____ Month(s): ____________ Year: ______ Length: ________

Cycle Day	1	2	3	4	5	6	7	8	9	10	11	12	13	14	15	16	17	18	19	20
Weekday																				
Date																				
Mucus Pattern																				
Sensation																				
Mucus Description																				
Sex																				
Cervical Position																				

Cycle Day	1	2	3	4	5	6	7	8	9	10	11	12	13	14	15	16	17	18	19	20
Time																				
Luteal Phase Count																				
Temperature	.8	.8	.8	.8	.8	.8	.8	.8	.8	.8	.8	.8	.8	.8	.8	.8	.8	.8	.8	.8
	.7	.7	.7	.7	.7	.7	.7	.7	.7	.7	.7	.7	.7	.7	.7	.7	.7	.7	.7	.7
	.6	.6	.6	.6	.6	.6	.6	.6	.6	.6	.6	.6	.6	.6	.6	.6	.6	.6	.6	.6
	.5	.5	.5	.5	.5	.5	.5	.5	.5	.5	.5	.5	.5	.5	.5	.5	.5	.5	.5	.5
98°	.4	.4	.4	.4	.4	.4	.4	.4	.4	.4	.4	.4	.4	.4	.4	.4	.4	.4	.4	.4
	.3	.3	.3	.3	.3	.3	.3	.3	.3	.3	.3	.3	.3	.3	.3	.3	.3	.3	.3	.3
	.2	.2	.2	.2	.2	.2	.2	.2	.2	.2	.2	.2	.2	.2	.2	.2	.2	.2	.2	.2
	.1	.1	.1	.1	.1	.1	.1	.1	.1	.1	.1	.1	.1	.1	.1	.1	.1	.1	.1	.1
	.0	.0	.0	.0	.0	.0	.0	.0	.0	.0	.0	.0	.0	.0	.0	.0	.0	.0	.0	.0
	.9	.9	.9	.9	.9	.9	.9	.9	.9	.9	.9	.9	.9	.9	.9	.9	.9	.9	.9	.9
	.8	.8	.8	.8	.8	.8	.8	.8	.8	.8	.8	.8	.8	.8	.8	.8	.8	.8	.8	.8
	.7	.7	.7	.7	.7	.7	.7	.7	.7	.7	.7	.7	.7	.7	.7	.7	.7	.7	.7	.7
	.6	.6	.6	.6	.6	.6	.6	.6	.6	.6	.6	.6	.6	.6	.6	.6	.6	.6	.6	.6
97°	.5	.5	.5	.5	.5	.5	.5	.5	.5	.5	.5	.5	.5	.5	.5	.5	.5	.5	.5	.5
	.4	.4	.4	.4	.4	.4	.4	.4	.4	.4	.4	.4	.4	.4	.4	.4	.4	.4	.4	.4
	.3	.3	.3	.3	.3	.3	.3	.3	.3	.3	.3	.3	.3	.3	.3	.3	.3	.3	.3	.3
	.2	.2	.2	.2	.2	.2	.2	.2	.2	.2	.2	.2	.2	.2	.2	.2	.2	.2	.2	.2
	.1	.1	.1	.1	.1	.1	.1	.1	.1	.1	.1	.1	.1	.1	.1	.1	.1	.1	.1	.1
	.0	.0	.0	.0	.0	.0	.0	.0	.0	.0	.0	.0	.0	.0	.0	.0	.0	.0	.0	.0

Luteal Phase: ________ **Ovulation:** __________

21	22	23	24	25	26	27	28	29	30	31	32	33	34	35
21	22	23	24	25	26	27	28	29	30	31	32	33	34	35
.8	.8	.8	.8	.8	.8	.8	.8	.8	.8	.8	.8	.8	.8	.8
.7	.7	.7	.7	.7	.7	.7	.7	.7	.7	.7	.7	.7	.7	.7
.6	.6	.6	.6	.6	.6	.6	.6	.6	.6	.6	.6	.6	.6	.6
.5	.5	.5	.5	.5	.5	.5	.5	.5	.5	.5	.5	.5	.5	.5
.4	.4	.4	.4	.4	.4	.4	.4	.4	.4	.4	.4	.4	.4	.4
.3	.3	.3	.3	.3	.3	.3	.3	.3	.3	.3	.3	.3	.3	.3
.2	.2	.2	.2	.2	.2	.2	.2	.2	.2	.2	.2	.2	.2	.2
.1	.1	.1	.1	.1	.1	.1	.1	.1	.1	.1	.1	.1	.1	.1
.0	.0	.0	.0	.0	.0	.0	.0	.0	.0	.0	.0	.0	.0	.0
.9	.9	.9	.9	.9	.9	.9	.9	.9	.9	.9	.9	.9	.9	.9
.8	.8	.8	.8	.8	.8	.8	.8	.8	.8	.8	.8	.8	.8	.8
.7	.7	.7	.7	.7	.7	.7	.7	.7	.7	.7	.7	.7	.7	.7
.6	.6	.6	.6	.6	.6	.6	.6	.6	.6	.6	.6	.6	.6	.6
.5	.5	.5	.5	.5	.5	.5	.5	.5	.5	.5	.5	.5	.5	.5
.4	.4	.4	.4	.4	.4	.4	.4	.4	.4	.4	.4	.4	.4	.4
.3	.3	.3	.3	.3	.3	.3	.3	.3	.3	.3	.3	.3	.3	.3
.2	.2	.2	.2	.2	.2	.2	.2	.2	.2	.2	.2	.2	.2	.2
.1	.1	.1	.1	.1	.1	.1	.1	.1	.1	.1	.1	.1	.1	.1
.0	.0	.0	.0	.0	.0	.0	.0	.0	.0	.0	.0	.0	.0	.0

Daily Notes

1 ____________________
2 ____________________
3 ____________________
4 ____________________
5 ____________________
6 ____________________
7 ____________________
8 ____________________
9 ____________________
10 ____________________
11 ____________________
12 ____________________
13 ____________________
14 ____________________
15 ____________________
16 ____________________
17 ____________________
18 ____________________
19 ____________________
20 ____________________
21 ____________________
22 ____________________
23 ____________________
24 ____________________
25 ____________________
26 ____________________
27 ____________________
28 ____________________
29 ____________________
30 ____________________
31 ____________________
32 ____________________
33 ____________________
34 ____________________
35 ____________________

Cycle: ___ Month(s): ___________ Year: _____ Length: ________

Cycle Day	1	2	3	4	5	6	7	8	9	10	11	12	13	14	15	16	17	18	19	20
Weekday																				
Date																				
Mucus Pattern																				
Sensation																				
Mucus Description																				
Sex																				
Cervical Position																				

Cycle Day	1	2	3	4	5	6	7	8	9	10	11	12	13	14	15	16	17	18	19	20
Time																				
Luteal Phase Count																				
Temperature	.8	.8	.8	.8	.8	.8	.8	.8	.8	.8	.8	.8	.8	.8	.8	.8	.8	.8	.8	.8
	.7	.7	.7	.7	.7	.7	.7	.7	.7	.7	.7	.7	.7	.7	.7	.7	.7	.7	.7	.7
	.6	.6	.6	.6	.6	.6	.6	.6	.6	.6	.6	.6	.6	.6	.6	.6	.6	.6	.6	.6
	.5	.5	.5	.5	.5	.5	.5	.5	.5	.5	.5	.5	.5	.5	.5	.5	.5	.5	.5	.5
98°	.4	.4	.4	.4	.4	.4	.4	.4	.4	.4	.4	.4	.4	.4	.4	.4	.4	.4	.4	.4
	.3	.3	.3	.3	.3	.3	.3	.3	.3	.3	.3	.3	.3	.3	.3	.3	.3	.3	.3	.3
	.2	.2	.2	.2	.2	.2	.2	.2	.2	.2	.2	.2	.2	.2	.2	.2	.2	.2	.2	.2
	.1	.1	.1	.1	.1	.1	.1	.1	.1	.1	.1	.1	.1	.1	.1	.1	.1	.1	.1	.1
	.0	.0	.0	.0	.0	.0	.0	.0	.0	.0	.0	.0	.0	.0	.0	.0	.0	.0	.0	.0
	.9	.9	.9	.9	.9	.9	.9	.9	.9	.9	.9	.9	.9	.9	.9	.9	.9	.9	.9	.9
	.8	.8	.8	.8	.8	.8	.8	.8	.8	.8	.8	.8	.8	.8	.8	.8	.8	.8	.8	.8
	.7	.7	.7	.7	.7	.7	.7	.7	.7	.7	.7	.7	.7	.7	.7	.7	.7	.7	.7	.7
	.6	.6	.6	.6	.6	.6	.6	.6	.6	.6	.6	.6	.6	.6	.6	.6	.6	.6	.6	.6
97°	.5	.5	.5	.5	.5	.5	.5	.5	.5	.5	.5	.5	.5	.5	.5	.5	.5	.5	.5	.5
	.4	.4	.4	.4	.4	.4	.4	.4	.4	.4	.4	.4	.4	.4	.4	.4	.4	.4	.4	.4
	.3	.3	.3	.3	.3	.3	.3	.3	.3	.3	.3	.3	.3	.3	.3	.3	.3	.3	.3	.3
	.2	.2	.2	.2	.2	.2	.2	.2	.2	.2	.2	.2	.2	.2	.2	.2	.2	.2	.2	.2
	.1	.1	.1	.1	.1	.1	.1	.1	.1	.1	.1	.1	.1	.1	.1	.1	.1	.1	.1	.1
	.0	.0	.0	.0	.0	.0	.0	.0	.0	.0	.0	.0	.0	.0	.0	.0	.0	.0	.0	.0

Luteal Phase: __________ **Ovulation:** ____________

21	22	23	24	25	26	27	28	29	30	31	32	33	34	35

21	22	23	24	25	26	27	28	29	30	31	32	33	34	35
.8	.8	.8	.8	.8	.8	.8	.8	.8	.8	.8	.8	.8	.8	.8
.7	.7	.7	.7	.7	.7	.7	.7	.7	.7	.7	.7	.7	.7	.7
.6	.6	.6	.6	.6	.6	.6	.6	.6	.6	.6	.6	.6	.6	.6
.5	.5	.5	.5	.5	.5	.5	.5	.5	.5	.5	.5	.5	.5	.5
.4	.4	.4	.4	.4	.4	.4	.4	.4	.4	.4	.4	.4	.4	.4
.3	.3	.3	.3	.3	.3	.3	.3	.3	.3	.3	.3	.3	.3	.3
.2	.2	.2	.2	.2	.2	.2	.2	.2	.2	.2	.2	.2	.2	.2
.1	.1	.1	.1	.1	.1	.1	.1	.1	.1	.1	.1	.1	.1	.1
.0	.0	.0	.0	.0	.0	.0	.0	.0	.0	.0	.0	.0	.0	.0
.9	.9	.9	.9	.9	.9	.9	.9	.9	.9	.9	.9	.9	.9	.9
.8	.8	.8	.8	.8	.8	.8	.8	.8	.8	.8	.8	.8	.8	.8
.7	.7	.7	.7	.7	.7	.7	.7	.7	.7	.7	.7	.7	.7	.7
.6	.6	.6	.6	.6	.6	.6	.6	.6	.6	.6	.6	.6	.6	.6
.5	.5	.5	.5	.5	.5	.5	.5	.5	.5	.5	.5	.5	.5	.5
.4	.4	.4	.4	.4	.4	.4	.4	.4	.4	.4	.4	.4	.4	.4
.3	.3	.3	.3	.3	.3	.3	.3	.3	.3	.3	.3	.3	.3	.3
.2	.2	.2	.2	.2	.2	.2	.2	.2	.2	.2	.2	.2	.2	.2
.1	.1	.1	.1	.1	.1	.1	.1	.1	.1	.1	.1	.1	.1	.1
.0	.0	.0	.0	.0	.0	.0	.0	.0	.0	.0	.0	.0	.0	.0

Daily Notes

1 ____________
2 ____________
3 ____________
4 ____________
5 ____________
6 ____________
7 ____________
8 ____________
9 ____________
10 ____________
11 ____________
12 ____________
13 ____________
14 ____________
15 ____________
16 ____________
17 ____________
18 ____________
19 ____________
20 ____________
21 ____________
22 ____________
23 ____________
24 ____________
25 ____________
26 ____________
27 ____________
28 ____________
29 ____________
30 ____________
31 ____________
32 ____________
33 ____________
34 ____________
35 ____________

Reflections

Reflections

Fertility Awareness Resources

The Fifth Vital Sign: Master Your Cycles and Optimize Your Fertility — thefifthvitalsignbook.com

- Using the Fertility Awareness Mastery Charting Workbook (free training video): thefifthvitalsignbook.com/workbookbonuses
- Free training videos: Cervical Mucus 101, BBT 101: thefifthvitalsignbook.com/bonuses
- *Fertility Awareness* Mastery Online Study Course: thefifthvitalsignbook.com/fam
- *Fertility Awareness* Mastery Live Coaching Program: thefifthvitalsignbook.com/live

Fertility Friday — fertilityfriday.com

- *The Fertility Friday* Podcast: fertilityfriday.com/podcast

Taking Charge of Your Fertility — tcoyf.com

- *Taking Charge of Your Fertility: The Definitive Guide to Natural Birth Control, Pregnancy Achievement, and Reproductive Health* by Toni Weschler

Justisse Method: Fertility Awareness and Body Literacy — justisse.ca

- *Justisse Method: Fertility Awareness and Body Literacy, A User's Guide* by Geraldine Matus

The Garden of Fertility — gardenoffertility.com

- *The Garden of Fertility: A Guide to Charting Your Fertility Signals to Prevent or Achieve Pregnancy — Naturally — and to Gauge Your Reproductive Health* by Katie Singer

FACTS: Fertility Appreciation Collaborative to Teach the Science — factsaboutfertility.org

Association of Fertility Awareness Professionals (AFAP) — fertilityawarenessprofessionals.com

Grace of the Moon by Sarah Bly — graceofthemoon.com

Fertility UK — fertilityuk.org

FEMM — femmhealth.org

Billings Ovulation Method — billings.life

Creighton Model FertilityCare System — creightonmodel.com

SymptoPro — symptopro.org

Quick Favour

If you enjoyed this book, may I ask a quick favour?

Would you take a moment to share how this book has resonated with you by reviewing it on Amazon?

Book reviews are one of the best ways to share the *Fertility Awareness Mastery Charting Workbook* and *The Fifth Vital Sign* with others.

Follow the link below to share your thoughts.

I also invite you to share your biggest takeaways from this book with other women in your life. Consider how your friends, family, and clients could benefit from the information contained here.

Thank you for helping me share this important message!

thefifthvitalsignbook.com/workbookreview

Ready to Start Charting Your Cycles?

Learning how to chart your cervical mucus and understanding your basal body temperature and cervical position is a complex process, especially if you've recently come off hormonal birth control or had a baby. Shave months (and in some cases years!) off the learning curve.

Fertility Awareness Mastery Online Course and Live Coaching Programs!

Learn how to chart your cycles, monitor your fifth vital sign with confidence,
and gain a unique window into your health and fertility.
Master your three main fertile signs — cervical mucus, basal body temperature, and cervical position — and benefit from this highly effective non-hormonal method of birth control for the rest of your life!

"I can't properly explain how empowering it is to feel so utterly in control of your body and your health. To work with someone who is so passionate and dedicated to helping you get there is beyond a pleasure."

— Emily W.

Lisa Hendrickson-Jack has taught hundreds of women to chart their cycles and gain confidence using fertility awareness for birth control, conception, and overall health. Learn how you can work with Lisa directly through her online course and LIVE coaching programs by following the link below.

thefifthvitalsignbook.com/fam

References

[1] Fehring, Richard J., Mary Schneider, and Kathleen Raviele. "Variability in the phases of the menstrual cycle." *Journal of Obstetric, Gynecologic, & Neonatal Nursing* 35, no. 3 (2006): 376–384.

[2] Frank-Herrmann, P., J. Heil, C. Gnoth, E. Toledo, S. Baur, C. Pyper, E. Jenetzky, T. Strowitzki, and G. Freundl. "The effectiveness of a fertility awareness based method to avoid pregnancy in relation to a couple's sexual behaviour during the fertile time: a prospective longitudinal study." *Human Reproduction* 22, no. 5 (2007).

[3] Hendrickson-Jack, Lisa. *The Fifth Vital Sign: Master Your Cycles and Optimize Your Fertility*. Fertility Friday Publishing Inc. (2019).

[4] Odeblad, Erik. "The discovery of different types of cervical mucus and the Billings Ovulation Method." *Bulletin of the Natural Family Planning Council of Victoria* 21, no. 3 (1994): 4; Klaus, Hanna. "Natural Family Planning—Is It Scientific? Is It Effective?" *Newman Lecture Series* 1 (2000): 6.

[5] Eggert-Kruse, Waltraud, Andreas Köhler, Gerhard Rohr, and Benno Runnebaum. "The pH as an important determinant of sperm-mucus interaction." *Fertility and Sterility* 59, no. 3 (1993): 617–628; Stein, Irving F., and Melvin R. Cohen. "Sperm survival at estimated ovulation time: prognostic significance." *Fertility and Sterility* 1, no. 2 (1950): 169–175; Ahlgren, Mats. "Sperm transport to and survival in the human fallopian tube." *Gynecologic and Obstetric Investigation* 6, no. 3-4 (1975): 206–214.

[6] Hilgers, Thomas W. (2004). *The Medical & Surgical Practice of NaPro Technology*. Omaha, NE: Pope Paul VI Institute Press, 107; Matus, Geraldine. *"Justisse Method: Fertility Awareness and Body Literacy: A User's Guide."* Justisse-Healthworks for Women (2009): 27.

[7] Hilgers, Thomas W. (2004). *The Medical & Surgical Practice of NaPro Technology*. Omaha, NE: Pope Paul VI Institute Press, 67–72; Matus, Geraldine. "*Justisse Method: Fertility Awareness and Body Literacy: A User's Guide.*" Justisse-Healthworks for Women (2009): 15–17.

[8] Ahlgren, Mats. "Sperm transport to and survival in the human fallopian tube." *Gynecologic and Obstetric Investigation* 6, no. 3–4 (1975): 206–214.

[9] Wilcox, Allen J., Clarice R. Weinberg, and Donna D. Baird. "Timing of sexual intercourse in relation to ovulation — effects on the probability of conception, survival of the pregnancy, and sex of the baby." *New England Journal of Medicine* 333, no. 23 (1995): 1517–1521; Stein, I.R., and Melvin R. Cohen. "Sperm survival at estimated ovulation time: prognostic significance." *Fertility and Sterility* 1, no. 2 (1950): 169–75; Ahlgren, Mats. "Sperm transport to and survival in the human fallopian tube." *Gynecologic and Obstetric Investigation* 6, no. 3–4 (1975): 206–214.

[10] Odeblad, Erik. "The discovery of different types of cervical mucus and the Billings Ovulation Method." *Bulletin of the Natural Family Planning Council of Victoria* 21, no. 3 (1994): 1–31; Fehring, Richard J., Mary Schneider, and Kathleen Raviele. "Variability in the phases of the menstrual cycle." *Journal of Obstetric, Gynecologic, & Neonatal Nursing* 35, no. 3 (2006): 376–384.

[11] Moghissi, Kamran S. "The function of the cervix in fertility." *Fertility and Sterility* 23, no. 4 (1972): 295–306; Klaus, Hanna. "Natural Family Planning—Is It Scientific? Is It Effective?" *Newman Lecture Series* 1 (2000): 4; Viergiver, Ellenmae, and W.T. Pommerenke. "Measurement of the cyclic variations in the quantity of cervical mucus and its correlation with basal temperature." *American Journal of Obstetrics and Gynecology* 48, no. 3 (1944): 321–328; Pommerenke, W.T. "Cyclic changes in the physical and chemical properties of cervical mucus." *American Journal of Obstetrics and Gynecology* 52, no. 6 (1946): 1023–1031.

[12] Guermandi, Ellade, Walter Vegetti, Massimiliano M. Bianchi, Anna Uglietti, Guido Ragni, and Piergiorgio Crosignani. "Reliability of ovulation tests in infertile women." *Obstetrics & Gynecology* 97, no. 1 (2001): 92–96.

[13] Su, Hsiu-Wei, Yu-Chiao Yi, Ting-Yen Wei, Ting-Chang Chang, and Chao-Min Cheng. "Detection of ovulation: a review of currently available methods." *Bioengineering & Translational Medicine* (2017): 238–246.

About the Author

Lisa Hendrickson-Jack talks about vaginas *a lot*. She's a certified Fertility Awareness Educator and Holistic Reproductive Health Practitioner who teaches women to chart their menstrual cycles for natural birth control, conception, and monitoring overall health. Drawing heavily from the current scientific literature, Lisa presents an evidence-based approach to fertility awareness and menstrual cycle optimization. She hosts the *Fertility Friday Podcast*, a weekly radio show devoted to helping women connect to their fifth vital sign by uncovering the connection between menstrual cycle health, fertility, and overall health. With well over a million downloads, *Fertility Friday* is the #1 source for information about fertility awareness and menstrual cycle health, connecting women around the world with their cycles and their fertility — something our education systems have consistently failed to do. When she's not researching, writing, and interviewing health professionals, you'll find her spending time with her husband and her two sons. To learn more, visit fertilityfriday.com.

Fertility Friday Publishing Inc.
lisa@fertilityfriday.com
fertilityfriday.com
thefifthvitalsignbook.com

Made in the USA
Las Vegas, NV
12 December 2021